PERIODIC TABLE (after Mendeléef)
(International atomic weights, 1952)

Period	Group 0	Group 1 A	Group 1 B	Group 2 A	Group 2 B	Group 3 A	Group 3 B	Group 4 A	Group 4 B	Group 5 A	Group 5 B	Group 6 A	Group 6 B	Group 7 A	Group 7 B	Group 8
1		1 H 1·008														
2 1st short period	2 He 4·003	3 Li 6·94		4 Be 9·013		5 B 10·82		6 C 12·01		7 N 14·008		8 O 16		9 F 19		
3 2nd short period	10 Ne 20·183	11 Na 22·997		12 Mg 24·32		13 Al 26·98		14 Si 28·09		15 P 30·975		16 S 32·066		17 Cl 35·457		
4 1st long period	18 A 39·944	19 K 39·1	29 Cu 63·54	20 Ca 40·08	30 Zn 65·38	21 Sc 44·96	31 Ga 69·72	22 Ti 47·90	32 Ge 72·60	23 V 50·95	33 As 74·91	24 Cr 52·01	34 Se 78·96	25 Mn 54·93	35 Br 79·916	26 Fe 55·85 27 Co 58·94 28 Ni 58·69
5 2nd long period	36 Kr 83·8	37 Rb 85·48	47 Ag 107·88	38 Sr 87·63	48 Cd 112·41	39 Y 88·92	49 In 114·76	40 Zr 91·22	50 Sn 118·70	41 Nb 92·91	51 Sb 121·76	42 Mo 95·95	52 Te 127·61	43 Tc —	53 I 126·91	44 Ru 101·7 45 Rh 102·91 46 Pd 106·7
6 3rd long period	54 Xe 131·3	55 Cs 132·91	79 Au 197·2	56 Ba 137·36	80 Hg 200·61	57 La 138·92 58–71 The rare earths *	81 Tl 204·39	72 Hf 178·6	82 Pb 207·21	73 Ta 180·88	83 Bi 209·0	74 W 183·92	84 Po 210	75 Re 186·31	85 At —	76 Os 190·2 77 Ir 193·1 78 Pt 195·23
7	86 Em 222	87 Fr —		88 Ra 226·05		89 Ac 227		90 Th 232·12		91 Pa 231		92† U 238·07				

Typical elements (Groups 1 A–7 A, Periods 1–3)

* The rare earths

58 Ce 140·13	59 Pr 140·92	60 Nd 144·27	61 Pm —	62 Sm 150·43	63 Eu 152·0	64 Gd 156·9	65 Tb 159·2	66 Dy 162·46	67 Ho 164·94	68 Er 167·2	69 Tm 169·4	70 Yb 173·04	71 Lu 174·99

† The transuranium elements

93 Np	94 Pu	95 Am	96 Cm	97 Bk	98 Cf

A SIMPLE GUIDE TO
MODERN VALENCY THEORY

A SIMPLE GUIDE TO
MODERN VALENCY THEORY

By

G. I. BROWN, B.A., B.SC.
Assistant Master, Eton College

With a Foreword by
L. E. SUTTON
M.A., D.Phil., F.R.S.

John Wiley & Sons Inc
New York, N.Y.

Published throughout the World except the United States
by Longmans, Green & Co., Ltd.

FIRST PUBLISHED 1953
NINTH IMPRESSION 1962

Made and printed in Great Britain by
William Clowes and Sons, Limited, London and Beccles

FOREWORD

Some time ago I happened to suggest to Mr. Brown that he might write a book about modern valency theory for sixth formers. It proved that he had been thinking this too: so we agreed that if he wrote it I would advise and help generally. The book now having been written, I might explain why one who does not teach sixth formers should take an interest in it.

Readers of this book presumably know already that advances in knowledge during the early years of this century broke down the classical divisions of chemistry; and that certain broad generalisations have been shown to apply to chemical behaviour. Progress in both theoretical and experimental research has steadily accelerated, however; and in the last twenty-five years there have been particularly rapid advances. These have greatly affected valency theory, which may now be deemed to cover the whole discussion of potential energy and configuration for atomic, molecular, and inter-molecular systems, and they have produced a much greater degree of unity. Because modern theory is reasonably powerful; because we can now ask some of the simpler—and therefore more difficult—questions with some hope of obtaining satisfying answers, the whole presentation of the subject is changing. There is a need, therefore, to formulate it in such a way that the essential ideas can be grasped by those who—if they will not take this amiss—are still near to beginning the subject. That is why those of us who are concerned with research and teaching come to be involved.

It is obvious that there are dangers and difficulties in this attempt. It would be easy to give the impression that modern theory is entirely successful, and that chemistry is now just a matter of ideas, with all hard work abolished. That, unfortunately, is not true: so such an impression would be at least as bad as the older one that chemistry is just a matter of fact. What is needed, then, is a just balance of emphasis between idea and facts. I think that Mr. Brown has been very successful in preserving it.

The difficulty of presentation is very great. Present-day valency theory concerns a very wide range of phenomena; it is abstract and elusive in its nature, it requires heavy mathematics for its rigorous development, and it calls for a great deal of knowledge and of seasoned judgment for its not-so-rigorous extensions. Of necessity, therefore, Mr. Brown has had to be dogmatic; but he has very skilfully kept dogma to a minimum and has made this minimum palatable.

The other difficulty is that such a book as this cannot possibly be fully up to date. Indeed, work in this field is so vigorous that it would not be easy to get agreement as to what is up to date at any instant. What can be said is that most of the ideas in this book are widely accepted. In five years' time most of them should still be deemed valid, though some will certainly have become obsolete. That is as much as anybody can expect.

L. E. SUTTON

Magdalen College,
Oxford

PREFACE

THIS book is intended to bridge the gap which the author believes to exist between the treatment of valency given in standard text-books of chemistry and that given in the more advanced works devoted entirely to valency.

It is intended for use by advanced sixth form pupils, by first-year university students, and by older chemists who are interested in modern developments but who may not have the time or inclination to study the more advanced works.

The treatment of the material is simple, concise, and mainly qualitative; mathematical considerations and experimental details have been reduced to a minimum. The aim has been to give a general account of modern valency theory which can be easily and readily grasped, and which will, it is hoped, help towards a fuller understanding of chemistry as a whole.

The work of Sidgwick and Pauling has contributed so greatly to the development of modern valency theory that constant reference to their writings is essential; I gratefully acknowledge the debt I owe to such sources. I am also very grateful to Dr. Sutton, my former tutor, for his continual interest and help. Any errors and omissions, however, are mine.

G. I. BROWN

CONTENTS

CHAPTER ONE

INTRODUCTION

1. The Importance of Valency. A study of chemistry, particularly of that branch of it known as inorganic chemistry, very soon reveals the wide variety and immense number of different chemical compounds. At a school level the learning of the subject often degenerates into an attempt to learn a seemingly endless catalogue of unrelated facts. In general there are too few threads to which a student can cling, and as a result it is difficult to obtain a real understanding.

Great progress has been made in recent years towards gaining a more fundamental understanding of chemical reactions. In the past, the treatment has been largely experimental. It has been known, for instance, that substance A combined with substance B to form substance C, and the conditions for such a reaction to take place have been worked out in some detail, as have the particular properties of A, B, and C. But the more fundamental questions as to why, or at least how, A and B combine to form C, why the properties of A, B, and C are what they are, and why X and Y, for instance, will not combine, were up till recent times left unanswered if not unasked.

The study of the problems which such questions raise is now termed the study of valency. The word originates from the late Latin, *valentia*, meaning strength, and it is with a study of the combining powers of chemical substances that valency is largely concerned.

2. The Dualistic Theory. The earliest theory of valency which had any success in explaining the known facts was put forward by Berzelius in 1812. Following, as it did, the discovery of the Voltaic pile in 1800 and the newly discovered results of early experiments on electrolysis, it is not surprising that the theory was of an electrical nature.

During electrolysis different substances appear at the two electrodes and Berzelius allotted to the atoms of each element an electrical polarity so that some atoms had a positive charge and some a negative one. Chemical combination, he said, took place between atoms with different charges as, for instance, in the formation of a molecule of sodium chloride from a positively charged sodium atom and a negatively charged chlorine atom:

$$Na^+ + Cl^- \longrightarrow NaCl$$

To account for the building up of larger molecules it was only necessary to assume an incomplete neutralisation of the opposite charges so that the formation of hydrated ferrous sulphate, for example, was envisaged according to the scheme

$$Fe^+ + O^- \longrightarrow FeO^+$$
$$S^+ + 3O^- \longrightarrow SO_3^-$$
$$FeO^+ + SO_3^- \longrightarrow FeSO_4^-$$
$$2H^+ + O^- \longrightarrow H_2O^+$$
$$FeSO_4^- + 7H_2O^+ \longrightarrow FeSO_4.7H_2O$$

Atoms in a molecule are, on this theory, held together by electrical attraction, and this idea is still an essential part of the modern theory of valency (see page 36).

3. The Theory of Types. The dualistic theory is clearly capable of considerable extension using the idea of residual electrical charges remaining on a compound after formation from its component atoms. As organic chemistry developed in the middle and later part of the nineteenth century, however, Berzelius' theory was replaced by a theory of types due originally to Dumas in 1839.

The dualistic theory failed to explain the fact that a supposedly positive atom could be replaced in a chemical compound by a supposedly negative atom without any great change in the nature of the compound. Thus acetic acid and chloracetic acid, or permanganic and perchloric acids are not dissimilar, though on the dualistic theory, a hydrogen or a manganese atom is quite distinct from a chlorine atom.

$$CH_3COOH$$
Acetic acid

$$HMnO_4$$
Permanganic acid

$$CH_2ClCOOH$$
Chloracetic acid

$$HClO_4$$
Perchloric acid

Furthermore, with the acceptance of Avogadro's hypothesis, it became clear that the molecules of many elements are polyatomic, e.g. H_2, O_2, Cl_2, so a theory was needed which could account for the linking together of two like atoms.

Dumas' idea was that there were certain fundamental types of chemical compound and that any element or group of elements in these types could be replaced, equivalent for equivalent, by another element or group of elements. This theory was developed by Williamson and Gerhardt, and the latter propounded four types, allotting known compounds to each type as illustrated below:

Hydrogen type	Hydrochloric acid type	Water type	Ammonia type
$\left.\begin{array}{c}H\\H\end{array}\right\}$	$\left.\begin{array}{c}H\\Cl\end{array}\right\}$	$\left.\begin{array}{c}H\\H\end{array}\right\}O$	$\left.\begin{array}{c}H\\H\\H\end{array}\right\}N$
Hydrocarbons, e.g.	Alkyl halides, e.g.	Alcohols, e.g.	Amines, e.g.
$\left.\begin{array}{c}CH_3\\H\end{array}\right\}$	$\left.\begin{array}{c}CH_3\\Cl\end{array}\right\}$ $\left.\begin{array}{c}C_2H_5\\Br\end{array}\right\}$	$\left.\begin{array}{c}CH_3\\H\end{array}\right\}O$	$\left.\begin{array}{c}CH_3\\H\\H\end{array}\right\}N$
Aldehydes, e.g.		Ethers, e.g.	Amides, e.g.
$\left.\begin{array}{c}C_2H_3O\\H\end{array}\right\}$		$\left.\begin{array}{c}CH_3\\CH_3\end{array}\right\}O$	$\left.\begin{array}{c}C_2H_3O\\H\\H\end{array}\right\}N$
Ketones, e.g.		Carboxylic acids, e.g.	
$\left.\begin{array}{c}C_2H_3O\\CH_3\end{array}\right\}$		$\left.\begin{array}{c}C_2H_3O\\H\end{array}\right\}O$	

Once again the theory is clearly capable of including a large number of known compounds, particularly when condensed types (Williamson), mixed types (Kekulé), and further simple types are introduced.

The theory was very successful in the realm of organic chemistry and eventually developed into the idea of *homologous series*. The main emphasis was on the structure of the molecule. The dualistic theory was concerned more with the nature of the particles combining than with their arrangement within a molecule.

A long and bitter controversy ensued between the exponents of the two rival theories, and, though the dualistic theory came into its own again when electrical ideas came to the fore as a result of Arrhenius' work in and after 1887, it is now realized that the two theories were dealing with different kinds of compound. In general the ideas of Berzelius apply in a modified form to what we now call electrolytes, whereas Dumas was dealing with non-electrolytes. In judging the merits of these old theories it is important to remember that they were developed at a time when atomic weights were not known with any accuracy and when it was far from certain that the formula of water was H_2O.

4. Valency as a Number. As the number of known chemical compounds grew, and as their formulae became known with more accuracy, the similarity of many of them became apparent. This was first noticed by Frankland, a supporter of Berzelius, in 1852, particularly in such compounds of nitrogen, phosphorus, and arsenic as *

$$NH_3 \qquad\qquad N_2O_3 \qquad N_2O_5 \qquad NH_4Cl$$
$$PH_3 \qquad PCl_3 \qquad P_2O_3 \qquad P_2O_5 \qquad PH_4Cl$$
$$AsH_3 \qquad AsCl_3 \qquad As_2O_3$$

* The formulae given are the modern ones; Frankland used different formulae for some of the compounds but the similarity was still clear.

in which the three elements are always combined with either 3 or 5 atoms of some other elements.

Frankland put forward the suggestion that an atom of an element had a certain 'combining power' which determined the number of atoms of another element with which it would combine. Thus nitrogen, phosphorus, and arsenic require 3 or 5 atoms of some other element to satisfy their 'combining power.'

This early suggestion led to the idea of the valency of an element being expressed as a number which gave a quantitative measure of the 'combining power' of the element. Moreover, the choice of hydrogen as the unit of 'combining power' made possible *the definition of the valency of an element as the number of atoms of hydrogen with which one atom of the element would combine.* The development of the relationship

$$\text{Atomic weight} = \text{equivalent weight} \times \text{valency}$$

stressed this idea of valency as a number.

There followed much argument as to whether the valency of an element was fixed or variable, but with the acceptance of the latter view in certain cases the simple statement became, and still is, a useful definition. It will be found in nearly all elementary chemistry books and is normally a schoolboy's first introduction to the word valency. By allotting the correct valency number (or numbers) to each atom or radical it is possible to build up the correct formulae for many chemical compounds. Thus, in general, if the formula of a compound is $A_x B_y$, A and B being elements or radicals, then

$$x \times \text{valency of } A = y \times \text{valency of } B.$$

The underlying ideas can be expressed pictorially by imagining that each atom has a certain number of arms or hooks which can each link with one arm or hook from another atom. Thus magnesium (valency 2) has two arms or hooks and oxygen (valency 2) has also two; one atom of magnesium will therefore combine with one atom of oxygen to form one molecule of magnesium oxide:

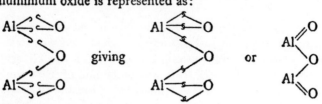

Aluminium (valency 3) has three arms or hooks so that aluminium oxide is represented as:

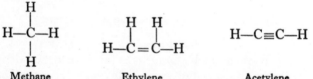

Other typical formulae are :

$$
\begin{array}{ccc}
\underset{\text{Methane}}{\overset{\displaystyle H}{\underset{\displaystyle H}{H-C-H}}} &
\underset{\text{Ethylene}}{\overset{\displaystyle H \quad H}{H-C=C-H}} &
\underset{\text{Acetylene}}{H-C\equiv C-H}
\end{array}
$$

and in the last two the idea of double and triple bonds has been introduced to satisfy the valencies of the atoms concerned.

These formulae convey no information as to the nature of the valency bonds indicated or as to the mechanism of their formation. Modern valency theory accounts for the mechanism of formation and gives much information as to the nature of the bonds.

Though useful, the idea of valency as a number must be treated with some caution. Applying the definition of valency (given above) to the oxides of nitrogen, and taking the valency of oxygen as 2, requires the assumption that nitrogen can have any valency from 1 to 5 :

Formula of oxide	.	N_2O	NO	N_2O_3	NO_2	N_2O_5
Valency of nitrogen	.	1	2	3	4	5

On the ideas of modern theory it is not always possible to express the valency of an element as a number.

5. The Periodic Table. The background against which inorganic chemistry is studied is the periodic table, a classification of the known elements in the order of their atomic weights. Newlands, Dobereiner, and others made early contributions towards this end but the classification was systematised in a clear-cut way by Mendeléef in 1869. All that is necessary is to arrange the elements in the order of increasing atomic weight; such an arrangement in the form suggested by Mendeléef is given on the front end-paper.

The elements fall into nine vertical groups, and elements in the same group have certain chemical and physical similarities. The horizontal groups are known as periods as shown. In this form of the table some of the vertical groups are subdivided into sub-groups known as sub-group A and sub-group B. This division comes into play in the higher periods, i.e. for the elements of higher atomic weight. The elements of lower atomic weight in the early periods, and at the head of each vertical group, are known as the typical elements and are not divided into sub-groups.

The three groups of elements placed in group 8 were originally called *transition*, or transitional, *elements*. They show some resemblances both to the element preceding them and to that following them and in that way they link up the first and second halves of the three long periods. The term transition element is now used in a wider sense to include elements other than those in group 8 (see page 34).

The original formulation of the periodic table has been modified in many ways to bring out certain features, and it is convenient at this stage to give (see front end-paper) an arrangement due to Thomsen and Bohr in which the typical elements are linked to their corresponding sub-groups by the vertical or diagonal lines. The importance of this arrangement is discussed on page 34.

One feature of the periodic table of immediate significance is that the numerical valency of an element is often equal either to the group number in which the element occurs or to 8 minus the group number.   Thus, in the example already quoted, nitrogen, phosphorus, and arsenic are found in group 5 and have valencies of 5 and 3.   This suggestion that if an element has two valencies then the sum of them will be equal to 8 was first put forward in 1904 as *Abegg's rule of eight*.   It will be seen in later chapters why the number eight should play such an important part.

CHAPTER TWO

OUTLINES OF ATOMIC STRUCTURE

1. Historical Development. The elucidation of the structure of the atom has led both to a much fuller understanding of the significance of the periodic table classification and to the foundation of modern valency theory. The development of today's ideas from those of Dalton 150 years ago is a long story of scientific achievement, but as it has often been told in detail it is only necessary here to list the more important stages. Moreover, so far as an understanding of valency is concerned, it is the results of work on atomic structure which are important and not the methods by which knowledge of the structure has been obtained.*

Historically the main stages of development may be summarised as follows:

(a) c. 1850–1897. Work on electric discharges in high vacua leading to the discovery of the electron. Determination of its mass (1/1840th of the mass of a hydrogen atom), charge (negative, and equal to the charge on a univalent ion) and velocity (variable).

(b) 1895. Röntgen's discovery of X-rays.

(c) 1896–c. 1910. Discovery of radioactive elements and of the three types of radiation, α-, β-, and γ-rays which they emit. α-rays found to consist of a stream of doubly ionised helium atoms, i.e. He^{++}; β-rays found to be a stream of electrons; γ-rays found to be 'X-ray like' light waves.

* For a student who has no knowledge of atomic structure a summary of the results obtained is given on page 13.

Discovery that electrons could be derived from other sources, e.g. by heating metals, or by allowing light to fall on a metal (photo-electric effect).

Realization that the electron is a component part of all matter.

(d) 1900.   Suggestion of the quantum theory by Planck.

(e) 1909–1911.   Rutherford's experiments on the bombardment of matter by α-rays and β-rays, leading to the idea of a nuclear atom in which there is a heavy, positively charged, central nucleus around which electrons are distributed in sufficient numbers to neutralise the positive nuclear charge.

(f) 1913–1914.   Moseley's work on X-ray spectra leading to his suggestion that, on passing from one atom to the next heavier in the periodic table arrangement, there is a unit increase of positive charge on the nucleus of the atom and an addition of one extra-nuclear electron.

(g) 1913.   Bohr's interpretation of atomic spectra.

2. The Position in 1914.   At this stage all atoms were envisaged as being made up of *protons* (hydrogen nuclei) and *electrons*, the former with unit mass and unit positive charge, and the latter with negligible mass and unit negative charge. The proton and electron were regarded as the fundamental particles from which all matter was made up.

				Mass	*Charge*
Proton	.	.	.	1	+1
Electron	.	.	.	(0)	−1

To account for the arrangement of the atoms in the periodic table it was necessary to assume that the nucleus of the atom contained both protons and electrons, and the following typical atomic structures illustrate the stage of development reached about 1914:

Hydrogen (A.W. = 1)   Helium (A.W. = 4)

(1p)   1e $\binom{4p}{2e}$ 2e

Lithium (A.W. = 7)   Uranium (A.W. = 238)

$\binom{7p}{4e}$ 3e $\binom{238p}{146e}$ 92e

The net positive charge on the nucleus is in all cases equal to the net negative charge of the *extra-nuclear* electrons so that the atom as a whole is electrically neutral. Moreover, the value of the positive nuclear charge or of the number of extra-nuclear electrons for the atom of any element is equal to the ordinal number of that element in the periodic table arrangement. This number is called the *atomic number*, and is of great importance as will be seen.

Although the ideas presented so far constituted a most definite advance on any previous suggestions, two problems remained. First, the packing together of positively charged protons and negatively charged electrons in unequal numbers in the nucleus of an atom was not a satisfactory arrangement so far as the electrical forces involved were concerned; secondly, the actual arrangement of the extra-nuclear electrons around the nucleus was unknown.

Both these problems have now largely been solved. Nuclear structure is discussed in the following section, and the arrangement of the extra-nuclear electrons in the next chapter.

3. **The Nucleus.** That scientists have been able to investigate so successfully the structure of atoms which no

one has ever seen is a remarkable achievement, but so much further work has been done that the investigation of the detailed structure of the nucleus of an atom is now in active progress. This is of great importance with regard to the stability of atoms and the development of atomic energy work, but, for our present purpose, it is not necessary to go very deeply into the matter since it is the extra-nuclear electrons which largely determine the chemical nature of an atom.

The difficulty of having positive and negative particles packed tightly together in the nucleus of an atom was resolved after the discovery by Chadwick in 1932 of a particle known as the neutron. Chadwick bombarded the element beryllium with α-rays from a radioactive substance and found that particles were emitted which were not affected by an electric or a magnetic field and were therefore electrically neutral. These particles are *neutrons*, with zero charge and unit mass.

It is now accepted that there are at least three fundamental particles—protons, electrons, and neutrons—of which atoms are composed, and the modern atomic structures put forward to replace those given on page 11 are shown on page 14.

4. Isotopes. A further development associated with the structure of the nucleus has been the conception and isolation of *isotopes—atoms with similar chemical properties but different atomic weights.* Since it is the extra-nuclear electrons which determine the chemical nature of an atom, two atoms with the same extra-nuclear arrangement will have the same chemical properties. Their having the same extra-nuclear arrangement, however, does not necessitate their having the same nuclear structure and it is this fact that leads to the possibility of isotope formation.

Thus there are three known isotopes of hydrogen with structures, names, and symbols as follows:

Protium (^{1}H)   Deuterium (^{2}H or D)   Tritium (^{3}H or T)

Normal hydrogen, as prepared in a laboratory, is a mixture of protium and deuterium in the proportions of about 6,000 to 1.   Tritium does not occur naturally, but it can be made in the laboratory.

Almost every element is now known to exist in similar isotopic forms, and the isotopes of uranium, represented as shown, are, currently, of particular interest.

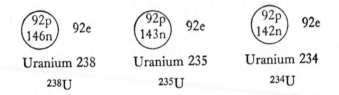

Uranium 238   Uranium 235   Uranium 234
^{238}U ^{235}U ^{234}U

The separation of isotopes is of great importance but it is not possible here to go into the methods employed.

5. Summary of Results of Work on Atomic Structure.
(a) Atoms are made up of three fundamental particles:

	Mass	Charge
Proton	1	+1
Electron	(0)	−1
Neutron	1	0

(b) An atom consists of a heavy, positively charged, central nucleus containing protons and neutrons, around which electrons are distributed. The positive charge on the nucleus is neutralised by the negative charge of the extra-nuclear electrons so that the atom as a whole is electrically neutral.

(*c*) Typical atomic structures are shown as follows:

Hydrogen (A.W. = 1)   Helium (A.W. = 4)

(1p) 1e   (2p / 2n) 2e

Lithium (A.W. = 7)   Uranium (A.W. = 238)

(3p / 4n) 3e   (92p / 146n) 92e

As one goes from atom to atom in the periodic table there is a unit increase in positive charge on the nucleus, and in the number of extra-nuclear electrons.

(*d*) The atomic number of an element represents its ordinal number in the periodic table (e.g. hydrogen, 1; uranium, 92), the net positive charge on the nucleus of the atom, or the number of extra-nuclear electrons.

(*e*) The chemical properties of an atom depend on the extra-nuclear electrons, and atoms may have the same number of extra-nuclear electrons but different nuclear structures. This possibility leads to the existence of isotopes —atoms with the same chemical properties but different atomic weights—as shown on page 13.

6. Note on Numerical Values. The numerical values of the masses of the fundamental particles and of the atomic weights of elements given in this chapter are those which are most easily remembered, but they are only near approximations. The accurate values depend on whether the masses are measured in terms of 1 atom of normal oxygen (the so-called chemical scale) or 1 atom of the ^{16}O isotope of oxygen (the so-called physical scale).

The accurate values are summarised below:

	Mass on chemical scale (O = 16)	Mass on physical scale (^{16}O = 16)
Proton	1·00730	1·00758
Electron	0·0005485	0·0005486
Neutron	1·00865	1·00894
Protium atom	1·00785	1·00813
Deuterium atom . . .	2·01418	2·01472

Normal oxygen is made up of a mixture of the three isotopes ^{16}O, ^{17}O, and ^{18}O, which accounts for the fact that masses based on the chemical scale are smaller than those based on the physical scale.

CHAPTER THREE

THE ARRANGEMENT OF EXTRA-NUCLEAR ELECTRONS IN AN ATOM

1. The Quantum Theory. Since it is the extra-nuclear electrons in an atom which determine its chemical properties, the detailed arrangement of these electrons is of fundamental importance. The working out of this arrangement is an amazing feat similar to the fitting together of a most complicated jig-saw puzzle or the solution of an elaborate cipher.

The first real progress in solving the problems involved came in the years following 1914 when Bohr applied the ideas of the quantum theory, first put forward by Planck in 1900, to the interpretation of spectroscopic data.

The essential idea of the quantum theory is that the energy of a body can only change by some definite whole-number multiple of a unit of energy known as the quantum. This means that the energy of a body can change (increase or decrease) by 1, 2, 3, 4 . . . n quanta, but never by $1\frac{1}{2}$, $2\frac{3}{4}$, 107·3, etc., quanta. It is rather like the fact that our currency can only change by 1, 2, 3, 4 . . . n farthings, but not by $1\frac{1}{2}$, $2\frac{3}{4}$, 107·3, etc., farthings.

Unlike the farthing, however, the value of the quantum is not fixed but is related to the frequency of the radiation which, by its emission or absorption, causes the change in energy. This relationship is expressed as

$$E \qquad = \qquad h \qquad \times \qquad \nu$$

| E (value of a quantum) | h (Planck's constant $= 6 \cdot 624 \times 10^{-27}$ erg-secs.) | ν (frequency of radiation) |

or, in terms of the wavelength (λ) of the radiation and the velocity of light (c),

$$E = \frac{h \cdot c}{\lambda}$$

so that it is a simple matter to calculate the value of the quantum corresponding to any known frequency.

This idea was originally developed by Planck in considering a vibrating body changing in energy by emitting or absorbing radiation of a frequency equal to the frequency of the vibrating body, but Einstein showed that the idea held more generally and that if the energy of a body changed from a value E_1 to a value E_2 by emission or absorption of radiation of frequency ν, then

$$E_1 - E_2 = n \cdot h \cdot \nu = \frac{n \cdot h \cdot c}{\lambda}$$

where n is an integer. It was this generalised statement of the quantum theory that was used by Bohr in his interpretation of spectra (see page 19).

Only a bare outline of the quantum theory has been given but it is adequate for our needs at this stage. Suffice it to say that the ideas expressed were necessitated by the failure of classical ideas to account for experimentally observed facts, and that the new ideas have been singularly successful in explaining a large number of such facts.

2. Spectra. Radiant energy is made up of a large number of waves of different wavelength and by using a spectrometer it is possible to 'sort out' the component parts of any radiation. Thus visible light is easily shown to be composed of red, orange, yellow, green, blue, indigo, and violet light, each colour corresponding to a group of waves of different wavelengths, as shown:

3,700	4,300	4,500	4,900		5,500	5,900	6,500		7,500
Violet	Indigo	Blue	Green		Yellow	Orange		Red	

The units in which the wavelengths are expressed are Angstrom units, 1A being equal to 10^{-8} cm.

Visible light represents but a small part of all radiation and a more complete representation of the possible types of radiation is given below:

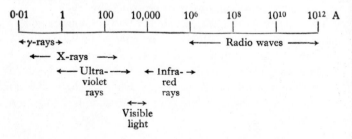

Characteristic spectra can be obtained from substances by causing them to emit radiant energy. This can be done in a variety of ways, e.g. by heating a substance or by subjecting it to electrical stimulation or excitation by using an electric spark, arc, or discharge; and a variety of so-called emission spectra can thus be obtained.

If the light from an electric filament lamp is examined by a spectroscope it is found to consist of all visible wavelengths, i.e. it gives a *continuous spectrum*. The light from a mercury vapour lamp, however, is made up of a limited number of wavelengths and its spectrum consists of a series of sharply defined lines each corresponding to a definite wavelength.

These are particular examples of the general fact that incandescent solids produce continuous spectra, whilst the excited vapour of an element gives rise to a so-called *line spectrum*.

3. Spectral Series. So far as the development of atomic structure is concerned a study of the line spectrum of hydrogen is of the greatest importance. This spectrum consists of a large number of lines corresponding to widely different frequencies, but over a period of time starting in 1885 it was found that many of the numerous lines could be fitted into series and hence were related to each other in some way.

These series, known after their discoverers as the Balmer (1885), Paschen (1896), Lyman (1915), and Brackett (1922) series, can be expressed in one overall formula:

$$1/\lambda = R(1/n^2 - 1/m^2)$$

where λ is the wavelength,* R a constant, known as Rydberg's constant, and n and m have integral values as follows:

Series				n	m
Lyman	.	.	.	1	2, 3, 4, etc.
Balmer	.	.	.	2	3, 4, 5, etc.
Paschen	.	.	.	3	4, 5, 6, etc.
Brackett	.	.	.	4	5, 6, 7, etc.

It is a remarkable experimental fact that so many apparently unrelated lines in a spectrum can be expressed by a simple formula. Line spectra of the alkali metals are also made up of similar series of lines known as the sharp, principal, diffuse, and fundamental series. The lines in these series can be related in a single formula as for the hydrogen spectrum.

4. Bohr's Interpretation of Spectral Series. Rutherford assumed that the extra-nuclear electrons circulated around the nucleus of an atom in orbits rather as the planets circulate round the sun, and atoms were pictured as minute solar systems.

---

* The reciprocal of the wavelength, $\frac{1}{\lambda}$, is called the wave number. It represents the number of vibrations per cm. It is often referred to as a frequency and denoted by v_0 or, simply, v, but the relation between the wave number and the real frequency is given by

$$\text{Wave number } (v_0) = \frac{1}{\text{wave-length } (\lambda)} = \frac{\text{frequency } (v)}{\text{velocity } (c)}$$

Bohr pointed out, however, that electrons, i.e. charged particles, could not circulate in an orbit without having a corresponding acceleration towards the centre of the orbit, and, according to the accepted electrodynamic theory of the time, an electric charge must radiate energy when it is accelerated.

If Rutherford's idea is correct, then, an atom would radiate energy continuously. This means that the extra-nuclear electrons would be continually approaching the nucleus until eventually they would come into contact with it. The atom would, in fact, undergo spontaneous destruction; nothing would exist. Moreover, the *continuous* emission of radiant energy does not account for the formation of *line* spectra.

To deal with these difficulties Bohr put forward suggestions which, in effect, deny the truth of older electrodynamic theories as applied to the motion of electrons. These are:

(*a*) that the extra-nuclear electrons in an atom could only rotate in certain selected orbits and that they did not then radiate energy. Such orbits were called *stationary states*, and

(*b*) that each stationary state corresponds to a certain energy level, i.e. that an electron in a certain stationary state had a certain energy, and that emission of radiant energy was caused by the movement of an electron from one stationary state to another of less energy. Conversely, absorption of energy took place by an electron moving into a stationary state of higher energy.

Bohr now applied the ideas of the generalised quantum theory (see page 17) to the change in energy caused by an electron moving from one stationary state to another. Thus, if the energy of one stationary state is E_1, and that of the next stationary state with lower energy is E_2, an electron passing from the first to the second would cause an energy change of $E_1 - E_2$, and an emission of radiation of frequency ν when

$$E_1 - E_2 = h \cdot \nu$$

As compared with the expression on p. 17, n is here equal to 1. Similarly absorption of radiation of frequency ν would cause an electron to pass from energy level E_2 to energy level E_1.

On this view the series observed in the line spectrum of

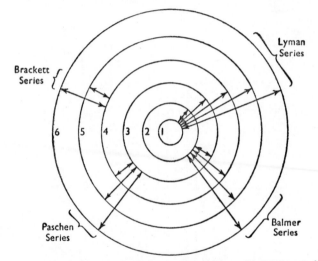

FIG. 1.   Illustration of the energy changes which an electron can undergo in moving between the various stationary states in an atom. (The diagram is not to scale, for the radii of the various stationary states are, in fact, proportional to the squares of the numbers allotted to them : see page 167)

hydrogen are explained by the various limited energy changes which an electron can undergo in moving between the various stationary states.   The general idea is made clear by a study of Fig. 1 which shows the various energy changes leading to the various lines in the spectrum.

The atom is in the *normal* or *ground state* when the electron is in the stationary state of least energy; when in any other state the atom is said to be excited. On excitation the electron moves into stationary states of higher energy content, and it is the return of the electron to stationary states of lower energy which results in the emission of radiant energy

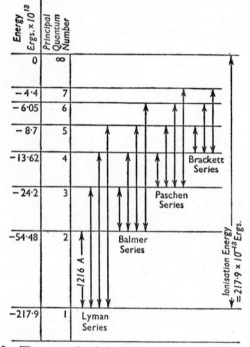

FIG. 2. The energy levels in the hydrogen atom (see p. 168)

and the formation of spectral lines. It is like lifting a ball up and letting it fall again, both the lifting and falling being done in definite stages.

For hydrogen and hydrogen-like spectra the Bohr theory is able to account for the observed spectral series in detail and with accuracy. The radii and energies of the various stationary states can be calculated as shown in the Appendix (page 166). Once the energies of the various stationary states are known, it is a simple matter to calculate the energy change occurring when an electron passes from one stationary state to another, and to relate the various energy changes to the observed spectral lines. Fig. 2 shows how this is done for hydrogen.

Various energy units are used. 1 electron-volt (or 1.59×10^{-12} ergs) is the energy gained by an electron in passing through a potential difference of 1 volt, and an energy change of 1 electron-volt per molecule or atom is equal to one of 23.05 kilocalories per gram-molecule or gram-atom.

Energy change and wave-length are related by $E = \dfrac{h \cdot c}{\lambda}$

(see page 17) so that the wave-length of the radiation corresponding to any energy change is easily calculated.

h has the value 6.624×10^{-27} erg-sec., and c, 2.99776×10^{10} cm. per sec. so that when an electron passes from an energy level of 217.9×10^{-13} ergs to one of 54.48×10^{-13} ergs (see page 168) there is an energy change of 163.42×10^{-13} ergs leading to a spectral line of wavelength λ given by

$$\lambda = \frac{6.624 \times 10^{-27} \times 2.99776 \times 10^{10}}{163.42 \times 10^{-13}} \quad \text{i.e. } 1.216 \times 10^{-5} \text{ cm.}$$

or 1,216A. This is the observed wave-length of the first line in the Lyman series (see Fig. 2).

5. Quantum Numbers. The extension of Bohr's ideas came about as a result of more detailed investigation of spectra. In particular, to account for the greater number of lines observed it was found necessary to increase the number of possible orbits in which an electron could exist in an atom. In other words, to explain the formation of all spectral lines it was necessary to allow for more energy changes within the atom. The term quantum number is used to label the various energy levels.

3

The number allotted to Bohr's original stationary states, visualised as circular orbits, is called the *principal quantum number*. The first orbit, i.e. that nearest the nucleus, has a principal quantum number of 1; the second orbit has a quantum number of 2, and so on. Alternatively, letters are used to characterise the orbits, the first being referred to as the K orbit, the second as the L, the third as the M, and so on.

A more detailed examination of spectra showed, however, that for each value of the principal quantum number there were several closely associated orbits so that the principal quantum number now represents a *group*, or *shell*, of orbits. To characterise the subsidiary orbits within a particular shell further quantum numbers are required. Altogether four quantum numbers are necessary but we need only be concerned with two of them at the moment. (The other two are introduced on pages 26 and 27.)

(a) *The principal quantum number*. This represents a group, or shell, of orbits as has been explained.

(b) *The subsidiary quantum number*. This represents the various subsidiary orbits within a shell; they may be visualised as elliptical orbits. Thus in a shell there may be subsidiary orbits denoted as the 1, 2, 3, 4 . . . or the s, p, d, f . . . orbits. The number of orbits in any one shell is, however, limited, and in dealing with the structure of atoms in their normal states it is only necessary to consider the following:

Principal quantum number or designation	1 or K	2 or L	3 or M	4 or N	5 or O	6 or P	7 or Q
Subsidiary quantum number or designation	1 or s	1 or s 2 or p	1 or s 2 or p 3 or d	1 or s 2 or p 3 or d 4 or f	1 or s 2 or p 3 or d 4 or f	1 or s 2 or p 3 or d	1 or s

Deciding to use numbers to represent the principal quantum number, and letters for the subsidiary quantum number, the list of orbits can be given as

$1s$	$2s$	$3s$	$4s$	$5s$	$6s$	$7s$
	$2p$	$3p$	$4p$	$5p$	$6p$	
		$3d$	$4d$	$5d$	$6d$	
			$4f$	$5f$		

Within an atom the electrons occupy the orbits listed above, though the number of electrons in each orbit and the orbits occupied in any particular atom are governed by a set of rules dealt with in the following section.

The use of quantum numbers may possibly be clarified by a simple analogy. Four quantum numbers are necessary to characterise any particular electron in any particular orbit. In a simple way this corresponds to a normal post-office address. To characterise a particular Mr. X it is necessary to allot a particular address to him, e.g.

> Mr. X,
> 114,
> High Street,
> Eton,
> Bucks.

The county corresponds to the principal quantum number, the town to the subsidiary quantum number, and the street and street number to the two quantum numbers not yet discussed (see pages 26 and 27).

6. Arrangement of Electrons in Orbits. The actual arrangement of electrons in the free atom of any element can be worked out from a study of the spectra of the element, and from its chemical properties in relation to its position in the periodic table. To account for all the known facts it has been necessary to put forward the following rules and principles which limit the possible electronic arrangements. Some of these may appear to be stated rather dogmatically but it is not possible to go more fully into the theoretical background in a book of this scope.

(a) *Total number of electrons in a shell.* The total number of electrons that can occupy any shell, i.e. that can have the same principal quantum number, is given by $2n^2$, where n is the principal quantum number concerned. Thus

Shell	K	L	M	N	O
Value of n	1	2	3	4	5
Maximum number of electrons in shell	2	8	18	32	50

(b) *The Pauli principle.* This states that *no two electrons in any atom can have the same four quantum numbers.* On the analogy given in the last section this means that no two Mr. X's can live in the same house.

It is clear from (a), however, that the K, (1), shell can contain two electrons. To agree with the Pauli principle it is necessary to assume that the two electrons have different spins; Mr. and Mrs. X, perhaps. In general, if two electrons occupy the same orbit they must have different spins, and, as electrons in the same orbit can only differ in having different spins, it follows that no orbit can contain more than two electrons. Moreover, a quantum number, known as the *spin quantum number*, must be allotted to each electron to characterise it.

For electrons in the shells other than the K shell a further complication arises. The L, (2), shell, for instance, can contain a maximum of eight electrons. Of these, two, with opposite spins, will be in the $2s$ level. The remaining six will be in the $2p$ level, but for all six electrons to be different it is necessary to subdivide the $2p$ level still further into three, so that each of the three may contain two electrons. These three $2p$ orbits may be envisaged as in different planes and can be denoted as the $2p_x$, $2p_y$, and $2p_z$ orbits (see Fig. 19, page 92).

This subdivision of p orbits into three, and a similar subdivision of d orbits into five and of f orbits into seven necessitates a fourth quantum number, known as the *magnetic quantum number*. For our purposes this is the least important quantum number since the energy of an electron in any of the three p orbits is the same unless the atom is placed in a strong magnetic field. When this happens, the field, so to speak, develops latent differences of energy since the three p orbits take up different positions with respect to the lines of force. This accounts for the *Zeeman effect*, a splitting of spectral lines when the source of emission is placed in a magnetic field.

(c) *The energy level of the various orbits.* The arrangement of electrons in an atom in its normal state is that which makes its energy a minimum, i.e. it is the most stable arrangement, within the limitations already mentioned.

The one electron in a hydrogen atom will, therefore, occupy the most stable orbit, and the second electron which is introduced in the helium atom will occupy the same orbit but will have a different spin. This particular orbit now contains a pair of electrons and is, therefore, full; a third electron, as in lithium, will occupy the next most stable orbit, and so on. The 'filling up' of the various orbits is very much like the 'filling up' of a concert hall; the best seats are occupied first.

Since the energies of the electrons in the various orbits can be derived from spectroscopic data, the detailed atomic structures of the elements can be built up. The results obtained are summarised in the diagram given in Fig. 3. Each circle represents an orbit which can be occupied either by a single electron or by two electrons with different spins.

The circles enclosed within a rectangle represent orbits of equal energy levels (except in a magnetic field—see page 27). The arrows indicate the order in which the orbits fill up.

Applying these results, but not differentiating between the three p, five d, or seven f levels, the arrangement of electrons in the atoms of the elements is shown on the back end-paper.

(d) *The rule of maximum multiplicity.* This empirical rule states that the distribution of electrons in a free atom between

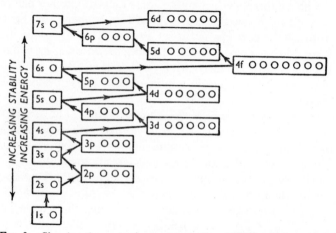

Fig. 3.   Showing the approximate comparative stabilities of the various orbits in an atom

the three p, five d, or seven f orbits is such that as many of the orbits as possible are occupied by a single electron before any pairing of electrons takes place.   Thus if three electrons are to be fitted into the three p orbits in any shell of a free atom, one will go into each of the three orbits.

A more detailed representation of the electrons showing their spins is made possible by the application of this rule, and Table 1 shows the electronic arrangements in the atoms having atomic numbers of 1 to 10.

TABLE 1. ILLUSTRATION OF THE SPINS OF ELECTRONS IN SIMPLE ATOMS.

		1s	2s	$2p_x$	$2p_y$	$2p_z$
1	H	↓				
2	He	↓↑				
3	Li	↓↑	↓			
4	Be	↓↑	↓↑			
5	B	↓↑	↓↑	↓		
6	C	↓↑	↓↑	↓	↓	
7	N	↓↑	↓↑	↓	↓	↓
8	O	↓↑	↓↑	↓↑	↓	↓
9	F	↓↑	↓↑	↓↑	↓↑	↓
10	Ne	↓↑	↓↑	↓↑	↓↑	↓↑

This more detailed arrangement is important, for, as will be seen later (page 77), unpaired electrons play an essential part in the formation of valency bonds.

7. **Wave Mechanics.** The dual nature of light as presented in the wave theory of Huyghens and the older corpuscular theory of Newton is well known. So far, an electron has been considered as an electrically charged particle, but, as in the case of light, it is also necessary to consider the wave nature of an electron when in motion.

de Broglie in 1924 first suggested that moving electrons had waves of definite wave-lengths associated with them. This theoretical prediction was demonstrated experimentally by Davisson and Germer in 1927, and it is now a well established fact that a stream of electrons can be diffracted by crystals acting as simple diffraction gratings, just as X-rays can (see page 119). Since it is only possible to account for diffraction phenomena in terms of waves it is necessary to assume that a stream of electrons behaves as a wave-like radiation similar to light or X-ray radiation.

The wave-length of the waves associated with moving electrons depends on the velocity of the electrons and is given by de Broglie's equation

$$\lambda = \frac{h}{mv}$$

where λ is the wave-length, h Planck's constant (see page 16), m the mass of the electron, and v the velocity; mv is, in fact, the momentum of the moving electron considered as a particle.

It is not easy to build up a pictorial representation of this new conception of an electron in motion, but, on the other hand, it is possible to treat the de Broglie waves associated with a moving electron mathematically. This has been done, particularly by Schrödinger, and involves the application of specialised mathematical methods known as wave mechanics, as opposed to the ordinary mechanics used in treating large moving particles such as billiard balls, trains, or planets. There is such a wide difference between the mass of an electron and the masses of a billiard ball or train or planet that it is not altogether surprising that the same treatment cannot be applied to both.

The broad results obtained by wave mechanical methods are in agreement with those obtained by Bohr, but the Bohr treatment was limited to very simple atoms. The methods of wave mechanics are not only more widely applicable but also give more detailed information.

It is not necessary, here, to go into the mathematical treatment. In general, the idea of a particle-like electron circulating in stationary states in well defined orbits is replaced by a representation of the motion of an electron as a three-dimensional 'wave pattern.' The 'wave pattern' for an electron or group of electrons can be expressed as a mathematical expression, known as a wave function and normally represented as ψ. These wave functions for any particular atom are obtained by solving a differential equation involving the total energy and the potential energy of the atom, but the number of wave functions, and hence the number of wave patterns, is limited by the fact that the differential equation has only got a certain number of valid solutions. The limited number of stationary states in the Bohr atom is, therefore, replaced by a limited number of 'wave patterns.'* The term *orbital* is often used to denote the rather more diffuse region in which the electron can be said to exist.

The energy values corresponding to any of the limited values of ψ can be obtained from the differential equation relating ψ with energy. These energy values correspond to the energy levels of the Bohr orbits (see page 169).

The application of wave mechanical considerations will be referred to later (see page 72). For most of what is to follow, the conception of an electron as a charged particle, and the Bohr model of the atom, serve as a near approximation which enables most of the ideas to be understood in a non-mathematical way.

* A two-dimensional illustration of the permissible 'wave patterns' can be given as follows. The only 'wave patterns' allowed are such that the wave will just fit into the path of the electron round the nucleus. Thus the 'wave patterns' depicted in Fig. 4 are permissible, but those in Fig. 5 are not.

Fig. 4. " Permissible "
wave patterns

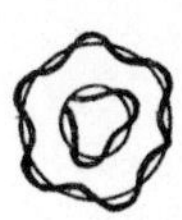

Fig. 5. " Forbidden "
wave patterns

CHAPTER FOUR

VALENCY BONDS

1. Types of Element. The valency of an element continued to be thought of as a number (as described on page 4) until the existence of electrons became well established and ideas of atomic structure began to develop. J. J. Thomson and Drude, about 1904, first put forward the general suggestion that valency bonds or links between atoms might be formed by a mechanism involving electrons.

Little progress was made until the arrangement of the extra-nuclear electrons in atoms had been worked out (see back end-paper). When this was done it was immediately clear that the position of an atom in the periodic table and its electronic structure were closely related. In particular, all the atoms in any one group of the table were found to have the same number of electrons in their outermost orbit, this number being equal to the group number. For example, the elements in group 1 have the structures given below:

Li	2.1
Na	2.8.1

K	2.8.8.1	Cu	2.8.18.1
Rb	2.8.18.8.1	Ag	2.8.18.18.1
Cs	2.8.18.18.8.1	Au	2.8.18.32.18.1
(Fr	2.8.18.32.18.8.1)		

The position of an element in the periodic table had always been associated with its valency (see page 8), and it was clear that the number of electrons in the outermost orbit might well be related to the valency.

Moreover, if electrons are going to take part in the formation of valency bonds it would be expected that the outermost electrons would play the most important part, for when two atoms approach each other before combining it will be the outermost electrons of the atoms which interact to the greatest extent. These outer electrons are, therefore, often referred to as *valency electrons*, and, for convenience, the orbits containing other electrons are often grouped together and referred to as the *core*. In group 1, therefore, the elements may be represented as:

Typical and *A* Sub-group
Elements   *B* Sub-group Elements
Core.8.1   Core.18.1

The differences between the *A* and *B* sub-groups in the periodic table arise from the fact that the penultimate orbit contains eight electrons in the *A* sub-group and eighteen in the *B* sub-group. This has important effects on the valencies of the elements concerned, as will be seen.

A complete examination of the electronic structures of the atoms reveals four types of element, and this sub-division is very useful. The types are summarised as follows.

(*a*) *The inert gases.* The arrangement of the electrons in the inert gases is as follows:

	1	2		3			4				5			6	
	s	*s*	*p*	*s*	*p*	*d*	*s*	*p*	*d*	*f*	*s*	*p*	*d*	*s*	*p*
He .	2														
Ne .	2	2	6												
A .	2	2	6	2	6										
Kr .	2	2	6	2	6	10	2	6							
Xe .	2	2	6	2	6	10	2	6	10		2	6			
Em .	2	2	6	2	6	10	2	6	10	14	2	6	10	2	6

In all cases all the orbits contain the maximum number of electrons. The shell is not necessarily complete but all the sub-levels within a shell are complete. Such an arrangement is obviously stable and explains the inability of the inert gases to enter into chemical combination. This stability of the inert gas structure is one of the foundation stones of modern valency theory.

(*b*) *Atoms with all except the outer shell complete.* These include all the elements, other than the inert gases, not included in frames in the Thomsen–Bohr arrangement of the periodic table given on the front end-paper.

The ions of these elements, if they form ions at all, are normally colourless and the elements have a more or less fixed valency, which if it does change does so by two units at a time. Compare, for instance, the valencies of carbon (4) and phosphorus (3 or 5) with those of iron (2 or 3) and nickel (2 or 3).

(*c*) *Atoms with the two outermost shells incomplete.* These include all the elements which are enclosed in a single frame in the Thomsen–Bohr arrangement. These elements are known as the *transition elements* (see page 7); they form coloured ions which are paramagnetic (see page 67), exhibit variable valency, and often possess marked catalytic activity.

(*d*) *Atoms with the three outermost shells incomplete.* These elements are known as the *rare earths*. They are a series of elements all with the same valency and great similarity in properties. Like the transitional elements they form coloured ions, which are paramagnetic, and exhibit catalytic activity.

The electronic structures given on the back end-paper show that all the rare earths have the same number of electrons in their two outer orbits, and that the series is formed by a filling up of the third outermost orbit from 18 to 32 electrons, i.e. a filling up of the $4f$ level.

Electrons in such an inner level play only a small part in determining the chemical properties of an element and that is why the rare earths are so similar as a group.

2. Types of Valency Bonds. The peculiar stability of

the electronic structures of the inert gases, as shown by their unreactive nature, led to the first hypotheses regarding the mechanism of valency bond formation. In all cases the underlying idea is that an atom combines with another atom in such a way that both atoms achieve an inert gas electronic structure. In this way compound formation is represented as a process resulting in greater stability.

This is a simple idea and the first suggestions as to the mechanism of valency bond formation were simple, too. As we shall see, however, they have required constant extension. The simple ideas will be discussed first under the main headings of *electrovalent* bond, *covalent* bond, and *dative* bond; some of the extensions will be mentioned in later chapters.

The three types of valency bond were originally thought of as distinct types, and in the early stages they are best dealt with in this way. It is, however, important to realise that these distinctions are made as a matter of convenience and that actual bonds may be intermediate.

3. Electrovalent Bond. Kossel suggested, in 1916, that those elements placed just before an inert gas in the periodic table could attain an inert gas structure by gaining electrons and hence forming negative ions. Thus chlorine with a structure 2.8.7 could become a chloride ion, Cl^-, with a structure 2.8.8 if it were to gain an electron.

Similarly, an element placed just after an inert gas could achieve an inert gas structure by losing electrons and forming positively charged ions, e.g. sodium, 2.8.1, could form a sodium ion, Na^+, with the inert gas structure, 2.8.

Both the chlorine and sodium ions would have stable electronic structures, and by combination would form sodium chloride,*

$$Na\bullet \;+\; \overset{\times\times}{\underset{\times\times}{\times\; Cl\; \times}} \longrightarrow [Na]^+ \left[\overset{\times\times}{\underset{\times\times}{\overset{\bullet}{\times}\; Cl\; \times}}\right]^-$$

* Only the valency electrons are shown

the two ions being held together in the compound by electro-static attraction (Coulomb forces).

The formation of such an electrovalent, or ionic, bond as it is called necessitates the gaining of electrons by one atom at the expense of another.   By attaining inert gas structures in the transference of electrons both atoms benefit so far as stability is concerned (see page 45).

Many simple compounds can be formulated on this idea. Electronegative elements (those preceding an inert gas) gain electrons and form negative ions; electropositive elements (those following an inert gas) lose electrons and form positive ions.   The following examples of electrovalent bond forma-tion will illustrate the further application of Kossel's sugges-tion:

(a) Calcium bromide, $CaBr_2$,

$$Ca \ \overset{\bullet}{\bullet} \ + \ \begin{matrix} \times \ \times \\ \times \ Br \ \times \\ \times \ \times \\ \times \ \times \\ \times \ Br \ \times \\ \times \ \times \end{matrix} \ \longrightarrow \ [Ca]_+^+ \ \begin{bmatrix} \times \ \times \\ \bullet \ Br \ \times \\ \times \ \times \end{bmatrix}^- \ \begin{bmatrix} \times \ \times \\ \bullet \ Br \ \times \\ \times \ \times \end{bmatrix}^-$$

(b) Potassium sulphide, K_2S,

$$\begin{matrix} K \bullet \\ \\ K \bullet \end{matrix} \ + \ \begin{matrix} \times \ \times \\ S \ \times \\ \times \ \times \end{matrix} \ \longrightarrow \ \begin{matrix} [K]^+ \\ \\ [K]^+ \end{matrix} \ \begin{bmatrix} \times \ \times \\ \bullet \ S \ \times \\ \times \ \times \end{bmatrix}^=$$

It will be seen that the formation of an electrovalent bond approximates to the original ideas of Berzelius (page 2) and that, in general, the bond is present in electrolytes; it is often referred to as an ionic bond.   More will be said about the mechanism and limitations of the formation of such a bond in Chapter 5.

4. Covalent Bond.   There are many compounds which cannot be formulated with electrovalent bonds, either because they are non-electrolytes, e.g. carbon tetrachloride, CCl_4, or because the atoms bonded together are the same, so that

neither would be expected to transfer an electron to the other, e.g. chlorine, Cl_2.

To account for the formation of such molecules, Lewis, in 1916, suggested that atoms might gain inert gas structures, not by complete transference of electrons, but by sharing electrons.

On this idea the chlorine molecule is represented as

$$\overset{\times\times}{\underset{\times\times}{\times}} Cl \overset{}{\underset{}{\times}} \overset{\bullet\bullet}{\underset{\bullet\bullet}{Cl}} \bullet$$

one electron from each atom being held in common by both. The *shared pair* of electrons constitutes what is known as a covalent bond. In carbon tetrachloride the molecule is represented as

and the double bond and triple bond of organic compounds, as exemplified by ethylene and acetylene, are represented by

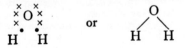

A shared pair of electrons represents one valency bond on the older system of writing the formulae (see page 6), and when it is not necessary to show in detail the arrangement of the electrons it is still convenient to denote a shared pair of electrons, i.e. a single covalent bond, by a single line. Water, for instance, may be represented as

$$\overset{\times\;\;\times}{\underset{\bullet\;\;\bullet}{\times\; O\; \times}} \qquad \text{or} \qquad \overset{O}{\diagup\;\diagdown}$$
$$H \quad\quad H \qquad\qquad\qquad H \quad\quad H$$

The covalent bond is found in general in non-electrolytes and between two electronegative atoms. The electrostatic binding force in the electrovalent bond is clearly visualised, but it is not so easy to see how and why a covalent bond can hold two or more atoms together. This and other problems of covalency bond formation are discussed in Chapter 6.

5. Dative Bond.* The introduction of the idea of the covalent bond alongside the electrovalent bond enabled most compounds to be formulated, but the arrangement of atoms in some compounds could still not be accounted for. This was the case, particularly, with a group of compounds known as *co-ordination compounds*, or, sometimes, as complex or molecular compounds, studied mainly by Werner in the years following 1891.

Such compounds are discussed in more detail in Chapter 7, and for the moment it is only necessary to pick out two examples, potassium ferrocyanide, $K_4[Fe(CN)_6]$, and hexamminocobaltic chloride, $[Co(NH_3)_6]Cl_3$. In solution, these compounds ionise to give K^+ plus $[Fe(CN)_6]^{--}$ ions, and Cl^- plus $[Co(NH_3)_6]^{+++}$ ions. The $[Fe(CN)_6]^{--}$ and $[Co(NH_3)_6]^{+++}$ ions are known as *complex ions*; in them the bond between the metal atoms and the CN and NH_3 groups remains intact in solution, and there is no ionisation into Fe^{++}, CN^-, Co^{+++}, or NH_4^+ ions.

It was to explain the formation of the bonds between the central metal atoms and the surrounding groups that the dative bond was suggested. Once formed, this type of bond is essentially the same as a covalent bond, i.e. it consists of a shared pair, but when a dative bond is formed between two atoms both the electrons are provided by one atom,

---

* The dative bond was originally called the co-ordinate bond because of its relation to co-ordination compounds, but dative bond is to be preferred so as to avoid any possible confusion with the crystallographic use of the words co-ordinated and co-ordination (see pages 40 and 61).

rather than each atom contributing one electron as in a covalent bond.

The structure of the CN^- ion and the NH_3 molecule are as below:

$$\left[\begin{array}{c} \overset{\times}{\underset{\circ}{\bullet}} C \overset{\times}{\underset{\times}{\times}} N \overset{\times}{\underset{\times}{\times}} \end{array} \right]^- \qquad \begin{array}{c} H \\ \overset{\times \bullet}{\underset{\bullet \times}{\times}} N \overset{\times}{} H \\ H \end{array}$$

and in each there is a pair of electrons not taking part in any valency bond formation. Such a pair of electrons is conveniently known as a *lone pair*.

On these grounds the formulae of potassium ferrocyanide and hexamminocobaltic chloride are given as

$$K_4^+ \left\{ \begin{array}{c} CN \\ NC\searrow \downarrow \nearrow CN \\ Fe \\ NC\nearrow \uparrow \searrow CN \\ CN \end{array} \right\}^{--} \qquad \left\{ \begin{array}{c} NH_3 \\ H_3N\searrow \downarrow \nearrow NH_3 \\ Co \\ H_3N\nearrow \uparrow \searrow NH_3 \\ NH_3 \end{array} \right\}^{+++} Cl_3^-$$

the charge on the ferrocyanide ion following from a combination of one Fe^{++} ion with six CN^- ions, and that on the hexamminocobalticion from a combination of one Co^{+++} ion and six uncharged NH_3 molecules.

The dative bond is represented in the above formulae by the $\rightarrow$ sign, and, in general, a single dative bond between two atoms A and B is written as $A \rightarrow B$, A being referred to as the *donor* and B as the *acceptor*.

This symbolism is very useful in indicating the origin of the electrons forming the bond, but in compounds containing both covalent and dative bonds the use of the two symbols, — (for a single covalent bond) and $\rightarrow$ (for a single dative bond), suggests a false differentiation between the bonds formed.

4

Aluminium chloride, for example, exists in the vapour state as Al_2Cl_6 and this molecule is often represented as

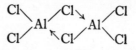

Al acting as the acceptor and Cl as the donor. There is, however, no real distinction between the four bonds in the ring, and a second conventional symbolism, common in American writing, avoids the use of two different symbols.

This second method of representing a dative bond depends on the fact that, when such a bond is formed, there is a partial transfer of two electrons from the donor to the acceptor. As a result of this, electric charges are developed on the atoms concerned, the donor becoming positively and the acceptor negatively charged. A single dative bond can therefore be written as $A^{\oplus}—B^{\ominus}$ instead of $A{\rightarrow}B$, and, on this scheme, aluminium chloride is written as

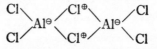

Because the bond has electric charges associated with it, it has been called a semi-polar bond or a semi-polar double bond; the term co-ionic has also been used. We shall, however, continue to use the name dative bond, and shall retain the use of the $\rightarrow$ symbol as a convenient way of showing the origin of the electrons forming the bond.

The following examples further illustrate the formation of dative bonds. To facilitate an understanding of the formulae the lone pair forming the dative bond is indicated:

(a) The ammonium ion, NH_4^+

In this ion the hydrogen atom acting as an acceptor has lost an electron and this gives the ion its positive charge. Once formed the bond is best represented as

and this makes it clear that there is no real distinction to be made between the four N—H bonds.

(b) Trimethylamine oxide, $(CH_3)_3NO$ (obtained by the oxidising action of hydrogen peroxide on trimethylamine)

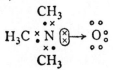

In this formula the three covalent bonds between nitrogen and carbon atoms use up three of the nitrogen's valency electrons but, as it has five, a lone pair remains, which is donated to the oxygen atom.

6. Other Types of Valency Bonds. Electrovalent, covalent, and dative bonds are the types normally found in the majority of compounds but some mention must be made of other interatomic forces, though, as they are relatively unimportant in general chemistry, they will not be discussed in any detail.

(a) *1-electron bond.* A normal covalent bond is made up of a shared pair of electrons but in the so-called hydrogen molecule-ion, H_2^+, there is only one electron available and the structure must, therefore, be represented as $[H \cdot H]^+$. This molecule-ion only occurs, however, in discharge tubes, and probably the only other compounds in which 1-electron bonds may play a part are the hydrides of boron (see page 142).

Between 1920 and 1930 Sugden developed a hypothesis that 1-electron bonds, called singlet linkages, were to be found in many compounds. He produced evidence to support his views, mostly based on the measurement of the parachor* of a substance, but the general modern view is that 1-electron bonds are very rare and can only occur between like, or very similar, atoms.

(*b*) 3-*electron bonds.* A bond composed of 3 electrons occurs more often than the 1-electron bond but it is still not very common. Probably the simplest example of a 3-electron bond is provided by the helium molecule-ion, which, like the hydrogen molecule-ion, is only found in discharge tubes. The representation is

$$[\text{He} \cdots \text{He}]^{+}$$

Other molecules in which 3-electron bonds occur are known as odd molecules since the total number of available valency electrons is odd. The following are the simplest examples:

(i) Nitric oxide, NO (see page 146),

$$\overset{\times}{\times}\text{N}\overset{\times}{\underset{\times}{\times}}\overset{\bullet}{\bullet}\text{O}\overset{\bullet}{\bullet}$$

(ii) Nitrogen peroxide, NO_2,

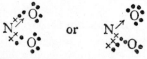

(iii) Chlorine dioxide, ClO_2,

---

* The parachor of a compound is a constant equal to $\dfrac{M}{D-d} \cdot \gamma^{\frac{1}{4}}$ where M is the molecular weight, D the density of the compound in liquid form, d the density as a vapour, and γ the surface tension.

It is also necessary to postulate the existence of a 3-electron bond in the oxygen molecule, O_2 (see page 164).

(c) *van der Waals' forces*. The departure of gases from the perfect gas laws is partially due to the existence of cohesive forces between the gas molecules. These forces, known as van der Waals' forces, after the man who first took them into account in modifying the gas equation from $P \cdot V = R \cdot T$ to

$$\left(P + \frac{a}{V^2}\right)(V - b) = R \cdot T,$$

also occur in liquids and solids. In these two states the forces are strong enough to hold the molecules together in spite of the opposing effect of thermal motion.

In the solid state, electrovalent substances are normally held together in *ionic crystals* by electrostatic attraction between ions (see page 61), and in many other crystals the atoms are all linked together by covalent bonds (see page 95). In some crystals, however, discrete molecules are held together by van der Waals' forces; crystals in which such forces are the main cohesive force are known as *molecular crystals*. Examples are the inert gases, oxygen, nitrogen, chlorine, iodine, and most organic substances, all in the solid form.

The detailed nature and origin of van der Waals' forces will not be discussed. For our present purpose it is sufficient to realise that it is a comparatively weak binding force.

(d) *The metallic bond*. Metals have very distinctive properties, and to account for this, particularly for the electrical conductivity, the idea of a special metallic bond is necessary.

The detailed work done on the nature of the bond need not concern us. Metals are invariably crystalline in the solid state and it is the binding between the atoms of the metal which constitutes the metallic bond. It general it may be said that a metallic crystal is made up of ions of the metal packed within the crystal but with free electrons moving in the interstices. The presence of the free electrons accounts for the electrical conductivity of a metal and for many of its other properties. The binding force is due to interaction between the positive ions and the free negative electrons.

(e) *The hydrogen bond.* Though it can only form one covalent bond a hydrogen atom may serve as a link between two atoms. Such a linkage is called a hydrogen bond; its nature will be discussed in Chapter 11.

CHAPTER FIVE

THE ELECTROVALENT BOND

1. Stable Ionic Structures. (*a*) *Inert gas structure.* In the simple treatment of the formation of an electrovalent bond given in the last chapter the discussion was limited to the formation of ions which had an inert gas structure. Thus an atom of sodium and an atom of chlorine, for instance, combine because by so doing they can each attain an inert gas structure which is a stable structure (see also page 56).

So far as negatively charged ions (anions) are concerned the only ions known are those with an inert gas structure, but to account for the formation of well-known cations it is necessary to assume stable structures which are not inert gas structures.

(*b*) 18-*electron group.* In the first place it is well known that many of the elements in the B sub-groups of the periodic table form ions, and these ions cannot have an inert gas structure. Zinc, 2.8.18.2, for example, forms a zinc ion, Zn^{++}, which must have the structure 2.8.18, and copper, 2.8.18.1, forms the cuprous ion, Cu^{+}, with the same structure, i.e. 2.18.8.

For elements in B sub-groups, then, an arrangement of 18 electrons in the outermost orbit of the ion formed from the element must have a certain degree of stability. The stability of an ion with such an electronic structure is not so great as that of an ion with an inert gas structure, and this explains the greater ease of formation of, for instance, a calcium ion, Ca^{++}, as compared with a zinc ion, Zn^{++}.

Moreover, an arrangement of 18 electrons in the outermost orbit of an ion is not very stable in elements in which the group of 18 electrons has only just filled up. In such cases one or more of the 18 electrons can be lost quite easily to form an ion with a greater charge. Copper, silver, and gold, for instance, form ions as below:

Cu	2.8.18.1	Ag	2.8.18.18.1	Au	2.8.18.32.18.1
Cu$^+$	2.8.18	Ag$^+$	2.8.18.18	Au$^+$	2.8.18.32.18
Cu^{++}	2.8.17	Ag^{++}	2.8.18.17	Au^{+++}	2.8.18.32.16

the more stable ions in each case being underlined.

It is clear that the arrangement of 18 electrons in the outermost orbit is not necessarily stable. This must be due to the charge on the nucleus not being high enough to hold the 18 group firmly, for in the elements with the next highest atomic numbers, i.e. the next stronger nuclear attractions, none of the 18 group ionise and only divalent ions are known. Thus

| Zn | 2.8.18.2 | Cd | 2.8.18.18.2 | Hg | 2.8.18.32.18.2 |
| Zn^{++} | 2.8.18 | Cd^{++} | 2.8.18.18 | Hg^{++} | 2.8.18.32.18 |

Trivalent ions of zinc, cadmium, and mercury are not known, i.e. the 18 electrons in the outermost orbit of the divalent ions are firmly held. Mercury does form a monovalent ion but this is due to another effect.

The argument can be expressed in others word by saying that the elements copper, silver, and gold, following as they do the transition series, behave in some ways as though they are included as transition elements, and a feature of these is their variable valency.

(c) *Transitional ions.* In considering ions formed by transitional elements (see page 34) it is necessary to assume that an ion with an outer group of 8–18 electrons is stable. The formation of two or more ions by this type of element is due to the small difference in stability between two or more alternative ionic structures.

For example, iron, 2.8.14.2, forms both ferrous ions, 2.8.14, and ferric ions, 2.8.13; cobalt, 2.8.15.2, forms both cobaltous ions, 2.8.15, and cobaltic ions, 2.8.14; and nickel, 2.8.16.2, forms both nickelous ions, 2.8.16, and nickelic ions, 2.8.15, though the formation of the latter is doubtful.

In this series of iron, cobalt, and nickel, the divalent ion becomes more stable as we pass from iron to nickel. In other words, nickel has a smaller tendency to lose electrons other than those in its outermost orbit than has iron. It is reasonable to assume that this is due to the greater nuclear charge in the case of nickel which can hold all the electrons more firmly.

Of these three possible structures for cations the order of stability is

     (i) inert gas structure,

     (ii) 18-electron group structure,

     (iii) transitional ion structure,

and an ion will be formed more easily the more stable is its structure. Furthermore, the more stable an ion is, the less tendency will it have to form complex ions, and ions do, in fact, form complex ions in the order (iii), (ii), (i). The formation of a complex ion by a simple ion is an attempt to increase its stability (see page 108).

2. The Inert Pair Effect. Some of the heavier B subgroup elements which would be expected to form only ions with an 18-electron group do, in fact, form other ions too. These ions have a charge of two units less than that of the expected ion, i.e. two electrons do not play their full part in ion formation. Such electrons are known as an inert pair, and their unexpected stability is attributed to possible extra stability of a pair of s electrons in any group.

The following well-established facts are all explained on this idea of an inert pair:

    (a) Thallium, 2.8.18.32.18.3, forms both the expected trivalent ion, Tl^{+++}, 2.8.18.32.18, and a monovalent ion, Tl^+, 2.8.18.32.18.2. Compounds of

monovalent thallium are more stable than those of
trivalent thallium, i.e. thallic salts are oxidising
agents.

The Tl^+ ion has the same structure as the Pb^{++}
ion (see (b) below) and this explains the likenesses
between certain thallous and plumbous compounds.
Thus thallous chloride, bromide, iodide, sulphate,
and sulphide are only slightly soluble like the corresponding plumbous compounds. The similarities
between thallous compounds and compounds of the
alkali metals are due to the fact that the thallous ion
has about the same size, and the same charge, as the
ions of the alkali metals (see page 131).

Indium, in the same group as thallium, shows the
same tendency, but it is not so marked, and the In^+
ion is at once converted to In^{+++} and the metal in
the presence of water.

Gallium forms no monovalent compounds.

(b) Tin, 2.8.18.18.4, and lead, 2.8.18.32.18.4, both
form the expected 4-valent ions, but they also form
divalent ions, Sn^{++}, 2.8.18.18.2, and Pb^{++},
2.8.18.32.18.2.

The effect of the inert pair is more marked in the
heavier element, i.e. lead, and the Sn^{++++} ion is
more stable than the Sn^{++} ion, whereas the Pb^{++}
ion is more stable than the Pb^{++++}. This explains
why stannous oxide and stannous chloride are
reducing agents, whereas plumbic oxide, PbO_2, and
lead tetrachloride are oxidising agents.

Moreover, lead tetrabromide and lead tetraiodide
do not exist but the corresponding compounds of tin
can be obtained.

(c) Both antimony and bismuth form trivalent ions,

Sb, 2.8.18.18.5 → Sb^{+++}, 2.8.18.18.2
Bi, 2.8.18.32.18.5 → Bi^{+++}, 2.8.18.32.18.2

and give definite trivalent salts. As with tin and lead the effect of the inert pair is more marked in the heavier element, i.e. bismuth. Bismuth, for instance, unlike phosphorus, arsenic, and antimony, does not form a pentachloride.

The effect of the inert pair in arsenic is apparent only in a few complex compounds.

(d) The fact that mercury vapour is monatomic, like the inert gases, points to mercury behaving as Hg, 2.8.18.32.18, and not as Hg, 2.8.18.32.18.2, i.e. a pair of electrons seem to be inert.

Further evidence of a less simple nature is available. The general conclusion is that the inert pair effect shows itself in the lower half of the table given below, i.e. in the heavier *B* sub-group elements:

Be	B	C	N	O	F
Mg	Al	Si	P	S	Cl
Zn	Ga	Ge	As	Se	Br
Cd	In	Sn	Sb	Te	I
Hg	Tl	Pb	Bi	—	—

The effect in any one vertical series becomes more marked as one passes down the series.

3. **Limitations to Formation of Ions.** Whether or not an atom will form an ion depends to some extent on the stability of the ionic structure which it might form. As ionisation depends on the gaining (anion formation) or losing (cation formation) of electrons, however, both the size of the atom and its atomic number are also important. The size of the atom determines the distance of the valency electrons from the nucleus. The atomic number determines the

positive charge on the nucleus, and it is this charge which holds the electrons in position.

The further an electron is from the nucleus, the less firmly is it held and the more easily can it be lost. Thus in the group series lithium, potassium, sodium, rubidium, caesium, the last atom, which is the largest, forms an ion most easily. Similarly, barium ionises more readily than strontium, calcium, or magnesium (see also section 4, page 53).

Once an electron has been lost from an atom the remaining ones are held more firmly and are not so easily lost. It is in this way that the formation of cations is limited to those with a charge of four units, and such highly charged ions are rare and only formed by large atoms. Tin and lead do form quadrivalent ions, but the smaller atoms of carbon and silicon do not. Similarly, aluminium forms a trivalent ion but the smaller atom of boron does not.

In the formation of anions, the positive charge on the nucleus of an atom may be able to hold one extra electron, and can sometimes hold two, but never more than two. In this case the smaller the anion the more easily can the nuclear charge hold the extra electrons, for in a small ion they are nearer to the nucleus than in a large one. As a result, anions are limited to those of hydrogen (see page 149), the halogens, oxygen, sulphur, selenium, and tellurium. In the halogen series, fluorine, with the smallest atom, most easily forms an anion. Thus mercuric, aluminium, and stannic fluorides are ionised compounds, whereas the corresponding chlorides are covalent.

From these general considerations it is possible to summarise the conditions favouring the formation of an ion. It can be stated that an ion will be formed most easily

(a) if the electronic structure of the ion is stable (see page 45),

(b) if the charge on the ion is small, and

(*c*) if the atom from which the ion is formed is small for an anion, or large for a cation.

These rules, in a slightly different form,* were first suggested by Fajans in 1924 and are usually referred to as *Fajans' Rules*.   If the conditions prevailing in any particular case do not favour the formation of ions then a covalent bond will probably be formed rather than an electrovalent bond.

The way in which the size and charge of the cation affects the types of chloride formed is well illustrated by the figures given in Table 2 for the melting points, boiling points, and equivalent conductivities (in fused state) of chlorides of typical and *A* sub-group elements.   The electronic structures of the ions formed is in all cases that of an inert gas so that no effect due to differences in the stability of the ions arises.

These chlorides clearly fall into two groups.   Those beneath the diagonal line are electrolytes and probably contain electrovalent bonds, whilst those above the line are non-electrolytes and probably contain covalent bonds.   It is not, however, justifiable, to be dogmatic about this on the evidence given, for the behaviour of a substance in the molten state does not necessarily have any significance as to its structure as a solid.   Nevertheless the diagonal demarcation line does seem to be related to the two tendencies indicated in the table, i.e. an increase in ionic charge along a horizontal period coupled with an increase in ionic size going down a vertical group.

The coupling of these two tendencies is also the reason

---

* Fajans used the conception of the atomic volume of an element, i.e. the atomic weight of the element divided by its specific gravity. This gives an approximate measure of the size of an atom of an element, and it follows, from what has been said above, that an ion will be formed most easily if the element from which the ion is formed has a low atomic volume for an anion, and a large atomic volume for a cation.

TABLE 2

THE MELTING POINTS (a), BOILING POINTS (b), AND EQUIVALENT CONDUCTIVITIES IN THE FUSED STATE (c), OF CHLORIDES OF TYPICAL AND A SUB-GROUP ELEMENTS

Increasing ionic charge →

Increasing ionic size ↓

		I	II	III	IV	V	VI
	(a)	HCl −114°					
	(b)	−85°					
	(c)	$<10^{-6}$					
		$LiCl$	$BeCl_2$	BCl_3	CCl_4	NCl_5	OCl_6
	(a)	606°	404°	−107°	−23°	Not formed	Not formed
	(b)	1,382°	488°	12·5°	76°		
	(c)	166	0·086	0	0		
		$NaCl$	$MgCl_2$	$AlCl_3$	$SiCl_4$	PCl_5	SCl_6
	(a)	800°	715°	—	−70°	148°	Not formed
	(b)	1,440°	(1,410°)	183°	57°	Decomps.	
	(c)	133	29	15×10^{-6}	0	0	
		KCl	$CaCl_2$	$ScCl_3$	$TiCl_4$	VCl_5	$CrCl_6$
	(a)	768°	774°	—	−23°	Not formed	Not formed
	(b)	1,415°	(1,600°)	(1,000°)	136°		
	(c)	103	52	15	0		
		$RbCl$	$SrCl_2$	YCl_3	$ZrCl_4$	$NbCl_5$	$MoCl_6$
	(a)	717°	870°	—	437° (25 atms.) Sublimes	194°	Not formed
	(b)	1,383°	(1,250°)	(700°)	—	241°	
	(c)	78	56	9·5	—	$2·2 \times 10^{-7}$*	
		$CsCl$	$BaCl_2$	$LaCl_3$	$HfCl_4$	$TaCl_5$	WCl_6
	(a)	640°	955°	—	432°	211°	275°
	(b)	1,303°	(1,800°)	(1,000°)	—	242°	347°
	(c)	67	65	29	—	3×10^{-7}*	2×10^{-6}*

$ThCl_4$
(a) 765°
(b) 922°
(c) 16

* Specific conductivities.

underlying the so-called diagonal relationships between certain elements in the periodic table.

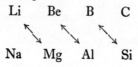

The elements joined by arrows have certain similarities and this is explained as being due to their comparative ease (or difficulty) of ionisation.

4. Ease of Formation of Ions. In the preceding sections it has been seen that some elements can form ions very readily whilst others never ionise. So far as the elements which do form ions are concerned, it is possible to arrive at a more quantitative measure of the ease with which they do so.

The *electrochemical series* (or affinity or reactivity series as it is sometimes called) gives some indication of the readiness with which an ion is formed, but since this arrangement depends on the measurement of *electrode potentials* * it is concerned with ions in solution. As will be seen (page 66), hydration of the ions takes place and this affects their ease of formation.

The series is, nevertheless, a useful simple guide in relating some chemical reactions and many properties of individual compounds. It is given in Table 3.

TABLE 3
THE ELECTROCHEMICAL SERIES
(Values in volts)

Cs	→ Cs$^+$	-2.93	Al	→ Al^{+++}	-1.28	H	→ H$^+$	0.00
Rb	→ Rb$^+$	-2.92	Zn	→ Zn^{++}	-0.76	Bi	→ Bi^{+++}	$+0.20$
K	→ K$^+$	-2.92	Cr	→ Cr^{++}	-0.56	Cu	→ Cu^{++}	$+0.35$
Ba	→ Ba^{++}	-2.84	Fe	→ Fe^{++}	-0.44	I	→ I$^-$	$+0.58$
Sr	→ Sr^{++}	-2.74	Cd	→ Cd^{++}	-0.40	Hg	→ Hg^{++}	$+0.80$
Na	→ Na$^+$	-2.71	Tl	→ Tl$^+$	-0.34	Ag	→ Ag$^+$	$+0.80$
Ca	→ Ca^{++}	-2.56	Co	→ Co^{++}	-0.29	Br	→ Br$^-$	$+1.08$
Li	→ Li$^+$	-2.09	Ni	→ Ni^{++}	-0.22	Cl	→ Cl$^-$	$+1.36$
Mg	→ Mg^{++}	-1.55	Sn	→ Sn^{++}	-0.14	Au	→ Au^{+++}	$+1.37$
			Pb	→ Pb^{++}	-0.12	F	→ F$^-$	$+2.80$

* The standard electrode potential of an element is the potential difference between the element and a solution containing the ions formed from the element in molar concentration, i.e. 1 gram-ion per litre. The electrode potential of hydrogen is arbitrarily chosen as zero, and other values are measured on this scale. The electrode potential is given as positive when the element is positively charged with respect to the solution, and negative when the element is negatively charged.

In considering the ease of ionisation other than in solution, the values of the *ionisation energy* for a cation and the *electron affinity* for an anion are of major importance.

The ionisation energy of an atom is a direct measure of the energy required to withdraw an electron from the atom against the attraction of the nuclear charge (see page 168). In other words it is the heat of reaction of the change

$$\text{Atom} + \text{energy} \rightarrow \text{cation} + 1 \text{ electron}$$

Values of ionisation energies can be measured experimentally by spectroscopic methods. It is not possible to go into the details of the methods employed but the results obtained, some of which are given in Table 4, are of great significance.

They show quantitatively some of the effects which have already been mentioned qualitatively and the following conclusions can be drawn:

    (a) For typical and *A* sub-group elements in the same group of the periodic table, the ease of ionisation increases as the radius of the atom increases. This is not so, however, for *B* sub-group elements.

    (b) Once one electron has been removed from an atom the others are held much more firmly and require more energy for withdrawal. In other words it is more difficult to form highly charged ions than those with a small charge.

The electron affinity of an atom is the energy given out when an extra electron is taken up by the atom. It is a measure of the heat of reaction of the change

$$\text{Atom} + 1 \text{ electron} \rightarrow \text{anion} + \text{energy} \ldots \text{X}$$

and may also be regarded as the ionisation energy of the anion, for the energy given out when an electron is added to an atom to form an anion is clearly equal to that required to remove an electron from the anion.

TABLE 4

IONISATION ENERGIES

(Values in kilocalories)

H → H+ 316		

| Li → Li+ 124 | Be → Be+ 214 | B → B+ 190 |

| Na → Na+ 119 | Be+ → Be++ 418 | B+ → B++ 575 |

The values given in this Table can be expressed as ionisation potentials in electron volts by dividing by 23·05 (see page 23).

K → K+ 101	Cu → Cu+ 177	Be → Be++ 632	B++ → B+++ 868
	Cu+ → Cu++ 464		B → B++++ 1,633
	Cu → Cu++ 641	Mg → Mg+ 176	Al → Al+ 137
		Mg+ → Mg++ 344	
Rb → Rb+ 96	Ag → Ag+ 173	Mg → Mg++ 520	Al+ → Al++ 431
Cs → Cs+ 91	Au → Au+++ 214		Al++ → Al+++ 651

Ca → Ca+ 140	Zn → Zn+ 215	Al → Al+++ 1,219
Ca+ → Ca++ 272	Zn+ → Zn++ 412	
Ca → Ca++ 412	Zn → Zn++ 627	

Sr → Sr+ 130	Cd → Cd+ 206
Sr+ → Sr++ 253	Cd+ → Cd++ 388
Sr → Sr++ 383	Cd → Cd++ 594

Ba → Ba+ 120	Hg → Hg+ 239
Ba+ → Ba++ 229	Hg+ → Hg++ 430
Ba → Ba++ 349	Hg → Hg++ 669

Unfortunately, it is not possible to measure electron affinities so easily as ionisation energies. Spectroscopic methods can be used, and one main method depends on a study of the change of equilibrium with temperature of the reaction given at X (page 54). Some values of electron affinities are given in Table 5.

TABLE 5

ELECTRON AFFINITIES

(Values in kilocalories)

H → H⁻ 16·4			
F → F⁻ 99	Cl → Cl⁻ 93	Br → Br⁻ 87	I → I⁻ 79
O → O⁻⁻ −150	S → S⁻⁻ −80		

The following conclusions can be drawn, and again they are in agreement with the more qualitative conclusions reached previously:

(a) In the halogen series it is easier to form an anion the smaller the atom is.

(b) Once one electron has been added to it an atom becomes negatively charged and the addition of more electrons is opposed. This explains the negative values of the electron affinities for the oxide and sulphide ions, and the much greater ease of formation of the monovalent halogen ions.

5. The Energy Changes in the Formation of an Electrovalent Bond.

In the formation of an electrovalent bond between two *free* atoms there are three factors to take into account:

(a) the ionisation energy in forming the cation,

(b) the electron affinity in forming the anion, and

(c) the electrostatic attraction between the two ions.

(*a*) and (*b*) can be measured experimentally as mentioned in the preceding section.   (*c*) can be calculated quite simply if the two ions are taken as being charged spheres and if the distance between them, *d*, is known.   This distance can, in fact, be measured (see page 130).

If two spheres are imagined with charges $+e_1$ and $-e_2$, at a distance *r* apart, then the attractive force is given by Coulomb's law as $F = \dfrac{e_1 \times e_2}{r^2}$. If now the spheres are displaced through a very small distance *dr*, the force may be taken as remaining constant, and the work done in displacement is given by force × distance, i.e. $F \cdot dr$.

In forming an electrovalent bond between two ions (represented as charged spheres) it is a matter of bringing the spheres to within a distance *d* of each other from a distance which by comparison is infinite. The energy released in doing this is, therefore, given by $\int_{\infty}^{d} F \cdot dr$, or $\int_{\infty}^{d} \dfrac{e_1 \times e_2}{r^2} \cdot dr$, and this gives the result $\dfrac{e_1 \times e_2}{d}$.

In the particular case of the formation of an electrovalent bond between free atoms of sodium and chlorine, the overall energy change will be

$$\text{Ionisation energy of sodium } (I_{Na}) - \text{Electron affinity of chlorine } (E_{Cl}) - \frac{e^2}{r_{Na} + r_{Cl}}$$

where r_{Na} and r_{Cl} are the ionic radii of the sodium and chloride ions and *e* is the ionic charge.   The process of bond formation will only take place if the energy change is negative, i.e. if the bonded ions are more stable than the free atoms, and this means that $\dfrac{e^2}{r_{Na} + r_{Cl}}$ must be greater than $I_{Na} - E_{Cl}$. In the example quoted this is, in fact, the case and hence a bond is formed.

So far we have considered only the formation of an electro-valent bond between *free* atoms of sodium and chlorine, but in the formation of a crystal of sodium chloride from solid sodium and gaseous chlorine other factors must be taken into account.

In the first place, the 'ion-pair' resulting from one free atom of sodium and one free atom of chlorine has a strong residual electric field, so that a large number of such 'ion-pairs' arrange themselves in the most stable way within an ionic crystal. This, of course, involves a further energy change, and the total energy change when free ions form together into a crystal is known as the *crystal energy*. The actual arrangement which ions may take up within a crystal is dependent largely on the geometric arrangement which will give the most stable structure. This is discussed in the next section.

Secondly, the formation of free sodium atoms from solid sodium, and of free chlorine atoms from gaseous chlorine, both demand the expenditure of some energy.

To calculate the heat of formation of sodium chloride, i.e. the heat of reaction of

$$\text{Na} \quad + \quad \tfrac{1}{2}\text{Cl}_2 \quad \rightarrow \quad \text{NaCl} \quad + \quad \text{H}$$

(solid)   (gaseous)   (crystalline)   (heat of reaction)

it is necessary then to take all the following energy factors into account:

(*a*) The ionisation energy of sodium, I_{Na}.

(*b*) The electron affinity of chlorine, E_{Cl}.

(*c*) The crystal energy of sodium chloride, C_{NaCl}.

(*d*) The energy required to dissociate solid sodium into free atoms. This is equal to the heat of sublimation, S_{Na}.

(*e*) The dissociation energy of gaseous chlorine, D_{Cl}.

All these energy factors are interrelated in the Born–Haber cycle,

$$
\begin{array}{ccc}
\underset{\text{(solid)}}{\text{Na}} + \underset{\text{(gaseous)}}{\tfrac{1}{2}\text{Cl}_2} & \xrightarrow{\;-H\;} & \underset{\text{(crystalline)}}{\text{NaCl}} \\[2ex]
{\scriptstyle +S_{Na}}\Big\downarrow \quad {\scriptstyle +D_{Cl}}\Big\downarrow & & \Big\uparrow {\scriptstyle -C_{NaCl}} \\[2ex]
\underset{\text{(free atoms)}}{\text{Na} + \text{Cl}} & \xrightarrow[\;]{\;I_{Na}-E_{Cl}\;} & \underset{\text{(free ions)}}{\text{Na}^+ + \text{Cl}^-}
\end{array}
$$

By Hess's law the energy change in the formation of crystalline sodium chloride must be the same however it is formed and it therefore follows that

$$ H = -S_{Na} - D_{Cl} - I_{Na} + E_{Cl} + C_{NaCl} $$

By measuring H, S_{Na}, D_{Cl}, I_{Na}, and calculating C_{NaCl}, the equation enables values of E_{Cl} to be determined, and when this is done for a series of metallic halides, for instance, the constancy of the values obtained for E_{Cl} is remarkable.

Similarly, if E_{Cl} is measured experimentally along with S_{Na}, D_{Cl}, and I_{Na}, and C_{NaCl} is again calculated, it is possible to obtain theoretical values for H, and these again agree remarkably well with experimentally determined values.

This discussion of the energy changes resulting from the formation of an electrovalent bond has been given to indicate the way in which it is possible to treat the matter quantitatively. The discussion has been simplified, particularly by regarding the ions as hard spheres, and by neglecting any detailed treatment of the repulsive force which comes into play as the electron shells of the two ions begin to overlap as they are brought closer together. It is this repulsive force which opposes the attractive force between the ions and results in the ions taking up an equilibrium position with a finite and measurable internuclear distance. The energy change as two ions are brought closer together is indicated

by the shape of the curve shown in Fig. 6. The shape of
the curve is a result of the competing contributions of the
attractive and repulsive forces to the energy of the system,

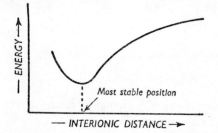

FIG. 6. The energy change as two ions are brought together

and shows that the ions actually arrange themselves at an
inter-nuclear distance which corresponds to the most stable
position.

6. The Geometric Arrangement of Ions in Crystals.
An 'ion-pair' of sodium chloride can be represented as in
Fig. 7, and though this is electrically neutral there is a

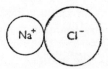

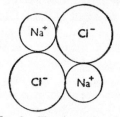

FIG. 7. Ion-pair of sodium
chloride

FIG. 8. Two ion-pairs of
sodium chloride

strong residual field. If a second 'ion-pair' is brought near
to the first the two will attract each other (just as two magnets
would) and arrange themselves as shown in Fig. 8. The
attraction of the oppositely charged ions is greater than the
repulsion of the similarly charged ones since the opposite
charges are nearer together.

If four 'ion-pairs' are brought together they will arrange themselves as shown in Fig. 9, and a larger number still will take up the arrangement represented in Fig. 10.

In this arrangement (Fig. 10), each sodium ion is surrounded octahedrally by six chloride ions, and each chloride ion by six sodium ions. This result agrees with the crystal structure of sodium chloride as observed experimentally by X-ray analysis (see page 119). This was, in fact, the first crystal structure to be elucidated by X-ray methods in 1913.

FIG. 9. Four ion-pairs of sodium chloride. The comparative sizes of the ions are not shown in this figure, but they are the same as in Fig. 8

It is clear that the sodium chloride molecule normally written as NaCl gives no real picture of the actual state of affairs. There is no such thing as a molecule of solid sodium chloride represented as made up of one particular sodium atom linked to one particular chlorine

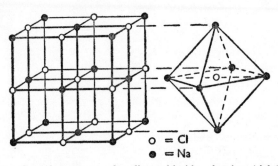

o = Cl
● = Na

FIG. 10. Crystal structure of sodium chloride, showing (right) the octahedral arrangement of six sodium ions around one chloride ion

atom. NaCl does, however, indicate the relative numbers of the two kinds of atom present.

The crystal type shown in Fig. 10 is known as an ionic crystal (see page 43) and is said to have a *co-ordination number* of 6, this number indicating the number of nearest neighbours of each ion in the structure.

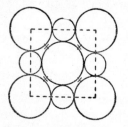

FIG. 11. Plan of the sodium chloride structure. The larger circles represent chloride ions (radius, 1·81Å) and the smaller circles, sodium ions (radius, 0·95Å)

It is clear from geometric considerations that the size of the ions in an ionic crystal must play a large part in determining the nature of the crystal. X-ray analysis of crystals enables ionic radii to be calculated (see page 130) and a plan of the sodium chloride crystal structure (Fig. 11) shows the comparative sizes of the two ions concerned.

If the size of the chloride ion is increased, i.e. if it is replaced by a bromide or iodide ion, there will come a time when the anions will come into contact at the points marked X. Any further increase in size would cause the anion to be pushed away from the cation and this would decrease the stability of the structure. Ultimately the ions would rearrange in some alternative, stabler structure. The same sort of considerations apply equally to the cation, and it is really the *radius ratio*, i.e.

$$\frac{\text{radius of smaller ion}}{\text{radius of larger ion}}$$

which is the controlling factor.

Almost all the alkali halides have the sodium chloride structure, but caesium chloride,

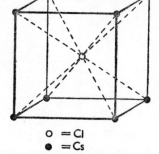

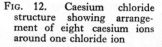

O = Cl
● = Cs

FIG. 12. Caesium chloride structure showing arrangement of eight caesium ions around one chloride ion

bromide, and iodide have an alternative arrangement in which each anion is surrounded by eight cations and vice versa. This structure is illustrated in Fig. 12 and has a co-ordination number of 8.

Other simple crystal structures are those in which each ion is surrounded by three others, or by four others. It is a straightforward geometrical problem to calculate the limiting radius ratio for each of the simple crystal structures mentioned, making the assumption again that the ions are spherical. The limiting values for the radius ratios are summarised below:

Structure	Co-ordination number	Limiting radius ratio
Triangular . . .	3	0·155–0·225
Tetrahedral . . .	4	0·225–0·414
Octahedral . . .	6	0·414–0·732
Cubic	8	Above 0·732

The discussion so far has been concerned with crystals made up of two simple ions, but many of the more complicated crystals are based on the same plan.

One, or both, of the simple ions in either the sodium chloride or the caesium chloride structure may be replaced by a charged group of atoms. Calcium carbonate, for instance, in the form of calcite or Iceland spar, is based on the sodium chloride structure; the sodium ions are replaced by calcium ions and the chloride ions by carbonate ions. In the carbonate ion, $CO_3^=$, the four atoms are held as a group by covalent bonds, with the carbon atom at the centre of an equilateral triangle and the oxygen atoms at the corners.

Other compounds with the sodium chloride structure are the oxides and sulphides of the alkaline earths, the chloride, bromide, and iodide of silver, CdO, FeO, CoO, NiO, MnO, MnS, and PbS.

Substances which crystallise with a caesium chloride

type of structure include caesium cyanide, thallous cyanide, thallous chloride, thallous bromide, and thallous iodide.

Ammonium chloride, bromide, and iodide crystallise with the sodium chloride structure above their transition temperatures, and with the caesium chloride structure below.

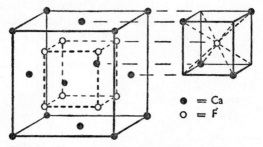

● = Ca
○ = F⁻

Fig. 13. Fluorite structure showing (right) the arrangement of four calcium ions around a fluoride ion

Such a change of structure with change of temperature is not uncommon.

For compounds of the type AX_2, the two commonest crystal structures are the fluorite, CaF_2, and the rutile, TiO_2, structures shown in Figs. 13 and 14. In these the co-ordination numbers are 8:4 and 6:3 respectively. In fluorite, for instance, each calcium ion is surrounded by eight fluoride ions at the corners of a cube, and each fluoride ion is surrounded by four calcium ions arranged tetrahedrally. As would be expected, it is the smaller ions which form the 6:3 co-ordinated structure. Thus a radius ratio greater than 0·73 leads to the fluorite structure, one between 0·414 and 0·73 leads to the rutile structure.

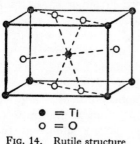

● = Ti
○ = O

Fig. 14. Rutile structure

A third related structure is the anti-fluorite structure which is the normal fluorite structure with the anions and cations interchanged. Some common compounds crystallising in these forms are listed below:

Fluorite structure	Rutile structure	Anti-fluorite structure
Difluorides of calcium, strontium, barium, cadmium, and mercury	Difluorides of nickel, cobalt, iron, manganese, magnesium and zinc Stannic oxide Lead dioxide Manganese dioxide	Oxides and sulphides of lithium, sodium, potassium

Many other types of ionic crystal are to be found but their structures cannot be discussed here.

7. Ions in Solution. One of the main features of a compound containing electrovalent bonds (or a bond which is predominantly electrovalent) is that they are electrolytes. This means that in the fused state or in solution in an ionising solvent, free ions exist. The majority of chemical reactions are studied in solution and most of the simple reactions take place between ions in solution, so that for many purposes the arrangement of ions in solid crystals is not of direct importance.

The formation of the free ions which exist in solution or in the fused state is, however, related to the arrangement of ions in the solid crystal, for to form free ions necessitates the breaking up of the crystal and this involves expenditure of energy equal to the crystal energy.

In the case of fusion, the energy is supplied by the heat required to bring about fusion, but direct heating does not necessarily cause dissociation into ions. Chemical decomposition may occur as, for instance, on heating sodium nitrate, calcium carbonate, or ammonium chloride, or, in a molecular crystal (see page 43), where discrete molecules are held together by weak van der Waals' forces, heating causes dissociation into molecules and not ions.

With regard to the formation of free ions in solution the electrostatic attractive forces in a crystal are broken down in a less direct way. The force between two charged bodies, e_1 and e_2, at a distance apart of d, is given by $F = \dfrac{e_1 \times e_2}{d^2 \times \epsilon}$, where ϵ is the dielectric constant of the medium separating the two charged bodies. The attractive force between ions in a crystal will be reduced in a medium of high dielectric constant, and ionising solvents are always liquids of high dielectric constant. The dielectric constant of water is 80, so that the force holding two ions together in air is 80 times as great as the force holding the same ions together in water. Other less common ionising solvents are liquid hydrogen cyanide, liquid hydrogen fluoride, liquid ammonia and liquid sulphur dioxide, with dielectric constants of 116 (at 20° C.), 83·6 (at 0° C.), 22 (at −33·4° C.), and 13·5 (at 15° C.) respectively.

The crystal energy of sodium chloride is 180 K.cals. per gm.-mol. and this is therefore the amount of energy required to form free ions from 1 gm.-mol. of crystalline sodium chloride. If, therefore, this amount of sodium chloride was dissolved in 1 litre of water, and all the energy was provided from the heat of the water, the solution would cool by −180° C. This is, of course, very much greater than the measured cooling effect and the necessary release of energy which accounts for this is caused by the *solvation* or *hydration* of the ions. This involves the linking of water molecules to the simple ion as discussed on page 111.

8. The Magnetic Moments of Ions.

Much information has been obtained as to the arrangement of electrons in ions from magnetic measurements, though it is only possible to give a brief picture of the work done here.

Substances may be classified as

(a) *paramagnetic*; they are drawn into a strong magnetic field such as that between the poles of a magnet, or

(b) *diamagnetic*; they tend to be drawn out of a magnetic field.

When suspended between the poles of an electromagnet a paramagnetic substance moves so as to take up a position parallel to the magnetic field, whilst a diamagnetic substance sets itself at right angles to the field (Fig. 15).

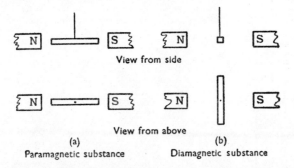

View from side

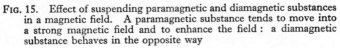

View from above

(a)   (b)
Paramagnetic substance   Diamagnetic substance

FIG. 15.   Effect of suspending paramagnetic and diamagnetic substances in a magnetic field. A paramagnetic substance tends to move into a strong magnetic field and to enhance the field : a diamagnetic substance behaves in the opposite way

Substances normally regarded as magnetic, e.g. iron, steel, cobalt, nickel, and magnetic alloys, are paramagnetic, but the degree of magnetism possessed by such substances is much greater than that of any others. They are said to be *ferromagnetic*.

The evidence regarding the arrangement of electrons in ions rests on the theoretical principle that an ion containing an unpaired electron (see page 28) is paramagnetic, whilst one in which all the electrons are paired is diamagnetic. Moreover, the magnetic moment of a paramagnetic substance can be measured in *Bohr magnetons*,* the value for an ion containing n unpaired electrons being $\sqrt{n(n+2)}$ magnetons. In this way a direct experimental measurement of the magnetic moment of an ion gives information as to the number of unpaired electrons in the ion. The expected results are given below:

Number of unpaired electrons . . .	0	1	2	3	4	5
Magnetic moment in Bohr magnetons .	0	1·73	2·83	3·87	4·90	5·92

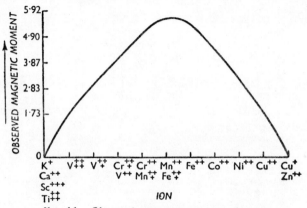

Fig. 16.   Observed magnetic moments of ions

* A rotating electron is equivalent to an electric current in a circular conductor and as such behaves as a magnet. The moment of such a magnet is given by

$$M = \frac{h \cdot e}{4\pi mc}$$

where e is the charge on the electron, m its mass, and c the velocity of light. When an orbit contains two electrons the magnetic moment due to one of them is compensated by the equal and opposite moment of the other. The unit of magnetic moment, known as the Bohr magneton, has the value given by the above expression; it is $9·18 \times 10^{-21}$ gauss-cm. for a single atom, or 5,564 gauss-cm. per gram molecule.

Ions in which all the orbits are full are diamagnetic and these include all the ions with an inert gas structure or an 18-electron group structure. The ions of the transition elements, however, contain incomplete orbits and are paramagnetic.

The observed magnetic moments of the ions formed by the elements in the first transition series, i.e. Sc, Ti, V, Cr, Mn, Fe, Co, Ni, and by the elements which precede and follow this series are shown graphically in Fig. 16. A comparison of the observed values with the calculated values given above leads to the following results:

Ion .	K^+Ca^{++} $Sc^{+++}Ti^{‡‡}$ Cu^+Zn^{++}	$V^{‡‡}$ Cu^{++}	V^{+++} Ni^{++}	$V^{++}Cr^{+++}$ Co^{++}	$Cr^{++}Mn^{+++}$ Fe^{++}	Mn^{++} Fe^{+++}
Number of unpaired electrons .	0	1	2	3	4	5

These results are in agreement with the electronic arrangements expected for these ions as shown in the following selected examples:

Ion	Structure of ion						Number of unpaired electrons
	$1s$	$2s$	$2p$	$3s$	$3p$	$3d$	
K^+ . .	2	2	2 2 2	2	2 2 2		0
V^{++++}. .	2	2	2 2 2	2	2 2 2	1	1
V^{+++} . .	2	2	2 2 2	2	2 2 2	1 1	2
V^{++} . .	2	2	2 2 2	2	2 2 2	1 1 1	3
Cr^{++} . .	2	2	2 2 2	2	2 2 2	1 1 1 1	4
Fe^{+++}. .	2	2	2 2 2	2	2 2 2	1 1 1 1 1	5
Fe^{++} . .	2	2	2 2 2	2	2 2 2	2 1 1 1 1	4
Co^{++} . .	2	2	2 2 2	2	2 2 2	2 2 1 1 1	3
Ni^{++} . .	2	2	2 2 2	2	2 2 2	2 2 2 1 1	2
Cu^{++} . .	2	2	2 2 2	2	2 2 2	2 2 2 2 1	1
Cu^+ . .	2	2	2 2 2	2	2 2 2	2 2 2 2 2	0

The electronic arrangements given assume the application of the rule of maximum multiplicity, i.e. that the five d orbits are occupied singly before any pairing takes place (see page 28). The agreement between calculated and experimental results in this field is, in fact, a demonstration of the truth of the rule.

The measurement of magnetic moments is also of use in elucidating the electronic arrangements in complex ions, and this topic is dealt with on page 109.

CHAPTER SIX

THE COVALENT BOND

1. The Conception of Resonance. The covalent bond has already been mentioned (see page 36) as comprising a shared pair of electrons between two atoms. On this basis, many compounds can be formulated with a satisfactory electronic structure but, whereas in the case of an electrovalent bond it is clear that atoms are held together as ions by electrostatic attraction, it is less easy to understand why a shared pair of electrons should hold two atoms together. The simplest * consideration of this problem involves an understanding of the conception of resonance.

This new conception introduces the idea that various 'possible' electronic structures for a substance may be involved in the 'actual' structure, and that the 'actual' structure will be more stable than any of the 'possible' structures involved.

The 'actual' structure to be visualised does not consist of a mixture of the various 'possible' structures. It is a single structure of its own, bearing some relation to the various 'possible' structures, but, as it is a structure which cannot be represented simply on paper, it is necessary to think of it in terms of structures which can.

It is difficult to obtain a visual picture of what resonance means. Palmer has given a helpful analogy in terms of a green letter which has been printed by first printing the letter in blue and then overprinting in yellow. The blue and the yellow letters correspond to the possible structures; the green to the actual one. A further analogy is

* The method of molecular orbitals provides an alternative approach to the problem; see page 156.

provided by the likenesses in any individual to his or her parents.

These analogies are very imperfect, and do not give any indication as to the greater stability of the 'actual' structure as compared with the 'possible' ones. This increase in stability due to resonance is very important and follows directly from an application of wave mechanics (page 29).

If it is supposed that a system has two 'possible' structures, I and II, they can each be represented by wave functions, ψ_I and ψ_{II}, which give the energy values of the structures they represent. By combining these two wave

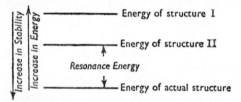

FIG. 17. Illustration of the increased stability of the " actual " structure caused by resonance between two " possible " structures, I and II

functions it is found that a third wave function will also represent the system and that this third function corresponds to a lower energy value, i.e. a higher stability. This can be illustrated as in Fig. 17.

The 'actual' structure is said to be resonating between structures I and II, or to be a *resonance hybrid* of structures I and II. The *resonance energy* is the extra stability of the 'actual' structure as compared with the most stable of the 'possible' structures. It will be seen that this extra stability precludes the possibility of the resonance hybrid structure being intermediate, as regards energy, between structures I and II, for it is more stable than either of them.

2. The Importance of Resonance. Resonance is a necessary extension of the application of wave mechanics to the problems of chemistry, but there is also a lot of direct experimental evidence supporting the conception. Some of this evidence will be discussed later (see Chapter 10).

For our immediate purpose the importance of resonance is threefold:

(a) It enables complicated systems, which cannot be described satisfactorily, to be discussed in terms of simpler structures which can be described. Many chemical properties which cannot be explained on any single structural formula are now known to be due to the existence of resonance.

(b) It clarifies the problem as to how a covalent bond can hold two atoms together.

(c) It does away with the older idea that electrovalent and covalent bonds are distinct types. It is now known that in a particular compound the bonds may be partially covalent and partially electrovalent.

A consideration of the problems raised by (a) will be given in dealing with various systems which are known to be resonating systems (see Chapter 10). The problems arising out of (b) and (c) are dealt with in the following sections.

3. The Electron Pair Bond. A satisfactory answer as to why a shared pair of electrons should link two atoms together is given in terms of resonance, and a consideration of the link in the hydrogen molecule best illustrates this.

The hydrogen molecule consists of two nuclei which will be distinguished as A and B, and two electrons which will be called 1 and 2. Electron 1 may be associated with nucleus A or with nucleus B, and similarly for electron 2. When the two nuclei are far apart they may be represented as

$$H_A^{\bullet 1} \qquad 2_B^{\bullet}H \qquad \text{Structure 1}$$
$$H_A^{\bullet 2} \qquad 1_B^{\bullet}H \qquad \text{Structure 2}$$

and a wave function can be calculated for each structure.

If the two nuclei in structure 1 are brought near to each other they will interact and the energy changes corresponding to the interaction can be calculated from the wave functions. On plotting the energy of the system against the internuclear distance line 2, Fig. 18, is obtained.

The same line represents the energy changes when the two nuclei in structure 2 are brought together.

If, however, the two structures are combined together, i.e. resonate, and the wave functions are treated accordingly, the change of energy of the system as the internuclear distance is varied is given by either line 1 or line 3 in Fig. 18.

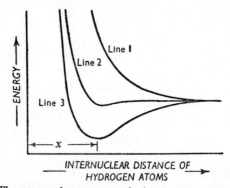

FIG. 18. The energy changes as two hydrogen atoms come together

Line 1 is the result obtained if the spins of electrons 1 and 2 are similar (or parallel); line 3 is obtained if the spins are different (or opposed).

Only line 3 shows a pronounced minimum and this corresponds to the formation of a stable hydrogen molecule with the atoms linked by a shared pair of electrons. The internuclear distance in the molecule is given by x. Lines 1 and 2 do not indicate any combination to form a stable molecule.

The following conclusions may be drawn:

    (a) the energy of the covalent bond in a hydrogen molecule is largely due to the resonance energy between the two possible structures 1 and 2,

(b) a covalent bond in a hydrogen molecule is only formed if the two electrons making up the bond have opposed spins.

As applied to covalent bonds in general these conclusions may be restated as follows:

(a) the energy of a covalent bond is largely due to the resonance energy corresponding to the interchange of two electrons between two atomic orbits,

(b) a covalent bond is only formed by two electrons with opposed spins.

These two statements go some way towards clarifying the mechanism involved in the formation of covalent bonds.

4. Limitations to Covalent Bond Formation. The statements given at the end of the preceding section mean, in other words, that for a covalent bond to be formed between two atoms, two electrons with opposed spins and a stable, but incomplete, orbit in each atom are required. Both these requirements limit the formation of covalent bonds as follows:

(a) *Requirement of a stable, incomplete, orbit.* In the early introduction to the covalent bond (page 36) it was suggested that elements formed covalent bonds in order to attain an inert gas structure, i.e. an octet of electrons in the outer orbit, and many compounds can be formulated on this idea. Such compounds as phosphorus pentachloride, PCl_5, sulphur hexafluoride, SF_6, iodine heptafluoride, IF_7, and osmium octafluoride, OsF_8, cannot, however, be formulated with an 'octet.' If represented in the normal way as

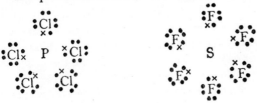

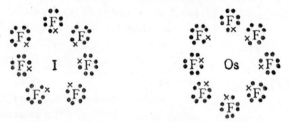

they demand ten, twelve, fourteen, and sixteen electrons in the outer orbit of the central atom.

All the atoms involving an 'expansion of the octet' are outside the first short period and, on purely chemical evidence, Sidgwick drew up a table of the maximum covalency which an atom can attain. This table is given below:

Element	Maximum covalency	Maximum number of shared electrons
H*	1	2
Li–F	4	8
Na–Br	6	12
Rb–U	8	16

* See Chapter 11, section 2, page 150.

The possible maximum for any particular element is not by any means always reached.

These covalency maxima can now be explained in terms of incomplete orbits which are available in an atom.

Hydrogen has only one stable incomplete orbit and is therefore limited to the formation of one covalent bond. Helium and other inert gases have no incomplete orbits and form no covalent bonds. The elements lithium to fluorine have four orbits in the L shell (one 2s and three 2p orbits) and are limited to four covalent bonds.

For elements above fluorine there are available nine orbits

in all in the M shell (one $3s$, three $3p$, and five $3d$). Of these the s and p orbits are the most stable and are used before the d orbits, but the d orbits can be used and this leads to the formation of more than four covalent bonds in many compounds containing elements above fluorine.

(b) *Requirement of opposed spins.* Electrons will not pair to form a covalent bond unless they have opposed spins, and this limits the bond formation of an element just as the necessity for incomplete orbits does. In general, the numerical valency of an element is equal to the number of unpaired electrons in its atom.

Table 1 on page 29 shows the spins of the electrons in the atoms of the first short period, and the relation between the number of unpaired electrons and the numerical valency is shown below:

Element	H	He	Li	Be	B	C	N	O	F	Ne
Number of un-paired electrons	1	0	1	0	1	2	3	2	1	0
Numerical valency	1	0	1	2	3	4	3	2	1	0

Except for beryllium, boron, and carbon, the number of unpaired electrons is equal to the numerical valency.

On these lines, the molecules of hydrogen, nitrogen, and fluorine are represented as being formed as follows:

(i) Hydrogen

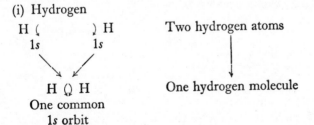

H ⟨   ⟩ H   Two hydrogen atoms
  1s   1s

   H ◖◗ H   One hydrogen molecule
One common
  1s orbit

(ii) Nitrogen

N ◯ ◯ ((( ))) ◯ ◯ N   Two nitrogen atoms
1s 2s   2p   2p 2s 1s

N ◯ ◯ ◯◯◯ ◯ ◯ N   One nitrogen molecule
1s 2s   Three   2s 1s
         common
         2p orbits

(iii) Fluorine

F ◯ ◯ ◯◯ ( ) ◯◯ ◯ ◯ F   Two fluorine atoms
1s 2s 2p   2p 2s 1s

F ◯ ◯ ◯◯ ◯ ◯◯ ◯ ◯ F   One fluorine molecule
1s 2s 2p One   2p 2s 1s
          common
          2p orbit

To account for the known valencies of beryllium (2), boron (3), and carbon (4), it is necessary to assume that some of the paired electrons must be uncoupled before the requisite number of bonds can be formed. This will require an input of energy, but such energy will be available from the heat of the reaction taking place when the covalent bonds are formed. The necessary changes are:

	1s	2s	2p			to	1s	2s	2p		
(a) Be	◯	◯				to	◯	(	(		
(b) B	◯	◯	(			to	◯	(	(	(	
(c) C	◯	◯	(	(		to	◯	(	(	(	(

and these changes give the required number of unpaired

electrons. The fact that of the four unpaired electrons in carbon three are in p orbits and one in an s orbit has important consequences which are discussed in section 10.

5. Effect of Covalency Maxima on Chemical Properties.

The fact that the different elements can form different numbers of covalent bonds as explained in the preceding section accounts for certain well-known chemical phenomena as follows.

(a) *Non-existence of nitrogen pentachloride.* The elements N, P, As, Sb, and Bi all form trichlorides, but nitrogen and bismuth do not also form pentachlorides. Bismuth pentachloride does not exist presumably through the operation of the inert pair effect (see page 47). Nitrogen pentachloride is not found since its formation would demand 5-covalent nitrogen, and as nitrogen is placed between lithium and fluorine in the periodic table its maximum covalency is 4.

This is but one particular simple example of the general fact that compounds of the elements Li–O are known which involve the elements in a 4-covalent form, but never in any higher covalency. Similarly, the elements from Na–Br are found in the 6-covalent form in various compounds but are never known to exert a higher covalency.

Fluorine is peculiar. It would be expected to reach a covalency of 4 but it does, in fact, never form compounds in which it is more than 1-covalent. This is presumably due to the small size of the fluorine atom and its corresponding reluctance, as indicated by Fajans' rules (see page 51), to form covalent compounds at all.

(b) *Stability of carbon compounds as compared with the corresponding silicon compounds.* Methane is not affected by treatment with water and sodium hydroxide but silicomethane reacts according to the equation

$$SiH_4 + 2NaOH + H_2O \rightarrow Na_2SiO_3 + 4H_2$$

This difference between the two hydrides is due to the fact that the carbon atom in methane has a fully shared octet of electrons, i.e. the carbon atom cannot act either as a donor or as an acceptor, whereas the silicon atom in silico-methane can act as an acceptor by expanding its octet. As the water molecule can act as a donor (there are lone pairs on the oxygen atom) it is able to 'attack' the silicon atom and a reaction results. The hydroxyl ions act catalytically.

The stability of C—C—C chains as compared with that of Si—Si—Si chains is also due, to some extent, to the fact that the silicon atoms are 'open to attack' by water whereas the carbon atoms are not. The C—C bond is, however, stronger than the Si—Si bond (see page 84) and this also accounts partly for the greater stability of carbon chains.

(c) *Hydrolysis of halides.* The various reactions between water and simple halides may be explained by considering the various possibilities of bond formation.

Many halides simply ionise in water and whether or not a particular halide will do this is determined by the application of Fajans' rules (see page 51 and Table 2). Other halides, e.g. CCl_4, SF_6, and SeF_6, do not react with water in any way; these are the ones in which the central atom has all its electrons fully shared and is also exerting its maximum covalency.

Of the remaining halides, some react with water to form hydrochloric acid and some to form hypochlorous acid. The former include BCl_3, $SiCl_4$, PCl_3, and PCl_5. In all these examples the central atom can hold more electrons than surround it in the simple halide, and can therefore act as an acceptor. Water can act as a donor so that the reactions which take place proceed via the formation of unstable intermediary compounds between the halide and water. The mechanism shown below for the reaction between water and silicon tetrachloride is typical:

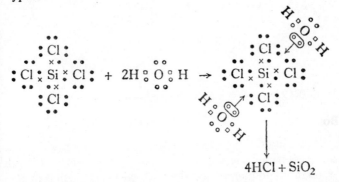

$$4HCl + SiO_2$$

The halides which react with water to produce hypochlorous acid are those in which the central atom has a lone pair and can therefore act as a donor but cannot (because it has already attained its covalency maximum) act as an acceptor. Examples are nitrogen trichloride, NCl_3,

and chlorine monoxide, Cl_2O,

In their reactions with water these molecules act as donors and the water molecule acts as an acceptor, HOCl splitting off from the unstable compound first formed. Thus with Cl_2O,

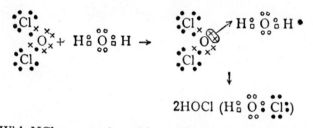

$$2HOCl \; (H\overset{\circ\circ}{\underset{\circ\circ}{O}}\overset{\bullet\bullet}{\underset{\bullet\bullet}{Cl}})$$

With NCl_3, ammonia and hypochlorous acid result,

$$NCl_3 + 3H_2O \rightarrow NH_3 + 3HOCl$$

It is interesting that though fluorine monoxide and nitrogen trifluoride are both known they do not react with water, as hypofluorous acid does not exist, so that the reaction mechanism postulated for the chlorine compounds cannot occur with the corresponding fluorine compounds.

6. Energy Changes in the Formation of Covalent Bonds. Determination of the bond energy in a diatomic molecule containing a covalent bond involves the measurement of the heat of formation of the molecule from its free atoms, or, alternatively, the heat of dissociation of the molecule into its free atoms. The bond energy A—B is equal to H where

$$\underset{\text{(atom)}}{A} + \underset{\text{(atom)}}{B} \rightarrow \underset{\text{(molecule)}}{A\text{—}B} + H$$

Normally this cannot be measured directly, as a compound is formed from molecules and not from free atoms, and also because a compound splits up on dissociation into molecules, and not free atoms, of its component elements.

To measure the heat of the reaction

$$H_2 + Cl_2 \rightarrow 2HCl + \boldsymbol{H}$$

* The bond between the O and H atoms in the molecule is probably a hydrogen bond rather than a normal dative bond (see Chapter 11).

for instance, does not give the bond energy of the H–Cl bond. What is required is the heat of the reaction

$$H + Cl \rightarrow HCl + Q$$

and to obtain this it is necessary to measure the heats of atomisation of both hydrogen and chlorine,

$$H_2 \rightarrow H + H - S$$
$$Cl_2 \rightarrow Cl + Cl - T$$

Q then becomes equal to $\frac{1}{2}(H + S + T)$.

The measurement of heats of atomisation is not easy, as a molecule cannot be completely dissociated into its free atoms merely by heating. The values can be obtained, however, from the change in the degree of dissociation with temperature, from the heat of sublimation, or by spectroscopic methods. Once the heats of atomisation have been obtained it is comparatively easy to measure the necessary heat of reaction.

For an oxide, for instance, the heat of reaction which has to be measured is the heat of combustion.

As a particular example the bond energy of the O—H bond will be calculated.

$$H_2 \rightarrow 2H - 103 \cdot 4 \text{ k.cal.} \quad \text{(Heat of atomisation of hydrogen)}$$

or $\quad 2H_2 \rightarrow 4H - 206 \cdot 8 \text{ k.cal.}$

$$O_2 \rightarrow 2O - 118 \cdot 2 \text{ k.cal.} \quad \text{(Heat of atomisation of oxygen)}$$

$$2H_2 + O_2 \rightarrow 2H_2O \text{ (gaseous)} + 115 \cdot 64 \text{ k.cal.} \quad \text{(2 × heat of combustion of hydrogen)}$$

It follows that

$$4H + 2O \rightarrow 2H_2O + 440 \cdot 64 \text{ k.cal.}$$

or $\quad 2H + O \rightarrow H_2O + 220 \cdot 32 \text{ k.cal.}$

And as there are two O—H bonds in one molecule of water the bond energy of the O—H bond is 110·2 k.cal.*

Values for other bonds can be obtained in similar ways and some of the results obtained are summarised in Table 6.

TABLE 6

BOND ENERGIES OF SINGLE BONDS

(Values in kilocalories)

H—H 103·4	C—C 81·6	N—N 38·4	O—O 34·9	S—S 63·8	F—F 33·3	F—H 132·4
	C—N 69·3	N—H 92·9	O—H 110·2	S—H 87·5	Cl—Cl 57·8	Cl—H 102·7
	C—O 81·5				Br—Br 46·1	Br—H 87·3
	C—H 98·8				I—I 36·2	I—H 71·4
	Si—Si 42·5					

By similar methods, results can be obtained for multiple bonds as shown in Table 7.

TABLE 7

BOND ENERGIES OF MULTIPLE BONDS

(Values in kilocalories)

C=C 146·1	C≡C 192·1	C=N 135·0	C=O 173·0	C≡O 256·0
N=N 97·6	N≡N 225·0			
O=O 96·0				

* This assumes that the two O—H bonds in one molecule of water have the same bond energy.

All the values given for bond energies are from data obtained by measurements on compounds for which it is possible (so far as is known) to allot a definite valency-bond formula. By using the values given, heats of formation of molecules with definite valency bond structures can be calculated, and these agree remarkably well with the values obtained from experimental heats of combustion.

Ethyl alcohol will be taken as an example to illustrate this. Its heat of combustion is 337 k.cal., i.e.

$$C_2H_5OH + 3O_2 = 2CO_2 + 3H_2O \text{ (liquid)} + 337 \text{ k.cal.} \quad \text{(i)}$$

The heats of combustion of solid carbon and gaseous hydrogen are 94·45 and 68·38 k.cal. respectively, i.e.

$$C \text{ (solid)} + O_2 = CO_2 + 94·45 \text{ k.cal.}$$

and $\quad H_2 \text{ (gaseous)} + \tfrac{1}{2}O_2 = H_2O \text{ (liquid)} + 68·38 \text{ k.cal.}$

Or, doubling the first and trebling the second equation,

$$2C \text{ (solid)} + 2O_2 = 2CO_2 + 188·9 \text{ k.cal} \quad \text{(ii)}$$

and

$$3H_2 \text{ (gaseous)} + 1\tfrac{1}{2}O_2 = 3H_2O \text{ (liquid)} + 205·14 \text{ k.cal.} \quad \text{(iii)}$$

Thus, by combining (i), (ii), and (iii),

$$2C \text{ (solid)} + 3H_2 \text{ (gaseous)} + \tfrac{1}{2}O_2$$
$$= C_2H_5OH + 57·04 \text{ k.cal.} \quad \text{(iv)}$$

57·04 k.cal. is, therefore, the heat of formation of ethyl alcohol from its elements in their normal form.

The heats of atomisation of solid carbon, gaseous hydrogen, and gaseous oxygen are 170·4, 51·7, and 59·1 k.cal., i.e.

$$2C \text{ (solid)} = 2C \text{ (atoms)} - 340·8 \text{ k.cal.}$$

$$3H_2 \text{ (gaseous)} = 6H \text{ (atoms)} - 310·2 \text{ k.cal.}$$

$$\tfrac{1}{2}O_2 \text{ (gaseous)} = O \text{ (atom)} - 59·1 \text{ k.cal.}$$

Combining these three equations with (iv) gives the result

2C (atoms) + 6H (atoms) + O (atom)
$$= C_2H_5OH + 767 \cdot 14 \text{ k.cal.}$$

$767 \cdot 14$ k.cal. is, therefore, the heat of formation of ethyl alcohol from its atoms.

The result calculated from bond energies is obtained simply by adding the energies of five C—H, one C—C, one C—O, and one O—H bonds, i.e. $(5 \times 98 \cdot 8) + 81 \cdot 6 + 81 \cdot 5 + 110 \cdot 2$. This gives the value of $767 \cdot 3$ k.cal. for the heat of formation of ethyl alcohol, which is in very good agreement with the previous value.

Heats of reaction can also be predicted from a knowledge of bond energies. The reduction of an ethylenic hydrocarbon to a paraffin, for instance, involves bond changes represented as follows:

$$
\begin{array}{ccc}
\underbrace{\text{C}{=}\text{C} \;+\; \text{H—H}}_{249 \cdot 5} & \rightarrow & \underbrace{\text{C—C} \;+\; 2\text{C—H}}_{279 \cdot 2} \\
146 \cdot 1 \qquad 103 \cdot 4 & & 81 \cdot 6 \qquad 2 \times 98 \cdot 8
\end{array}
$$

It will be seen that the reduction involves an evolution of $29 \cdot 7$ k.cal. and this is in very good agreement with experimental values.

7. Ionic Character of Covalent Bonds. A covalent bond between an atom A and an atom B may be represented as $A\overset{\bullet}{\underset{\times}{}}B$, and an electrovalent bond as $[A]^+[B\overset{\bullet}{\underset{\times}{}}]^-$. In the former case the two electrons are shared between A and B; in the latter they are both held by B and not, to any extent, by A. There has been much discussion as to whether these two types of bond are extreme, distinct types or whether transitional types might occur. It is now known that in the majority of cases transitional types of bond do occur, and there is probably no such thing as a true covalent bond.

Experimental evidence for this conclusion is provided by the results obtained from dipole moment measurements described on page 127. The theoretical background rests on wave mechanical treatment and the conception of resonance.

In discussing the electron pair (covalent) bond in the hydrogen molecule in section 3 the two possible structures allotted to the system were

$$H_A^{\bullet 1} \qquad 2^{\bullet}_B H \qquad \text{Structure 1}$$
$$H_A^{\bullet 2} \qquad 1^{\bullet}_B H \qquad \text{Structure 2}$$

and it was seen that resonance between these structures led to the formation of a bond.

Taking the argument further, two other structures are possible, both involving ions. Thus both electrons 1 and 2 may be associated with atom A or with atom B and this leads to the two structures

$$H_A^{\bullet 1 \bullet 2} \qquad _B H \qquad \text{Structure 3}$$
$$H_A \qquad 2 \bullet 1^{\bullet}_B H \qquad \text{Structure 4}$$

These last two structures are relatively unstable as compared with the first two, since the ionisation energy of hydrogen is high (316 k.cal./gm. mol.) and the electron affinity low (16·4 k.cal./gm. mol.). When the two ions in structures 3 and 4, then, are far apart, the energy change in their formation is − 299·6 k.cal./gm. mol., but as the ions are brought together they attract each other strongly and this stabilises the system to some extent.

The bond in a hydrogen molecule must be considered, then, not in terms of wave functions representing structures 1 and 2 only, but by wave functions which take into account the existence of structures 3 and 4 as well. When this is done it is found that the contribution of structures 3 and 4 to the possibilities of resonance makes the bond formed more stable. The so-called covalent bond in a hydrogen molecule has, therefore, some ionic character.′

7

In the case of the hydrogen molecule bond the ionic character is small because of the relative instability of the structures 3 and 4, but for other bonds the ionic structures play a larger part. In a bond between an electropositive atom A and an electronegative atom B the ionic structure A^+B^- may have a similar stability to the covalent structure A—B. The structure A^-B^+ will not play a very large part for if it is easy to form A^+B^- it cannot also be easy to form A^-B^+.

The stability of the A^+B^- form will clearly depend on the relative electronegativities of A and B. The greater the difference between their electronegativities the more stable will A^+B^- be and the more ionic in character will be the bond between A and B.

The actual contribution of the A^+B^- structure to the actual bond between A and B could be measured on the following lines:

Actual bond energy found experimentally $= H$

Bond energy if bond were truly covalent $= Q$

Extra stability caused by resonance between
truly covalent bond and ionic bond $= H - Q$

Unfortunately, a truly covalent bond is, in most cases, hypothetical and therefore Q cannot be measured. Pauling has attempted to obtain values of Q, however, by postulating that the bond energy of a truly covalent bond A—B must be intermediate between the bond energies of the bonds A—A and B—B. For, because the bonds A—A and B—B are between like atoms they are essentially, if not truly, covalent, i.e. the ionic bonds in these cases play only a small part as they are not very stable.

He has assumed in the first place that the bond energy of the truly covalent bond A—B (E_{AB}) is the arithmetic mean of the energies of the bonds A—A (E_{AA}) and B—B (E_{BB}), i.e.

$$E_{AB} = \frac{E_{AA} + E_{BB}}{2}.$$

In more accurate, but less simple, considerations he has taken the geometric instead of the arithmetic mean, i.e.

$$E_{AB} = \sqrt{E_{AA} \times E_{BB}}.$$

In either case the difference between the calculated value of E_{AB} and the measured value of the bond energy of the actual A—B bond gives a measure of the resonance energy due to the partial ionic nature of the actual bond. The results summarised below illustrate this.

	H—F	H—Cl	H—Br	H—I
Calculated bond energy, E_{AB} (arithmetic mean of E_{AA} and E_{BB} *)	68·4	80·	74·8	69·8
Actual bond energy of bond A—B	132·4	102·7	87·3	71·4
Ionic resonance energy . .	64·0	22·1	12·5	1·6

(Values are given in k.cal./gm. mol.)

   * Slightly different figures are obtained if the geometric mean is taken instead of the arithmetic mean.

8. The Electronegativity Scale. As expected, the results summarised above show that as we pass from the H—F to the H—I bond there is a decrease in the ionic nature of the bond as indicated by a decrease in the ionic resonance energy. This is due to the greater difference in electronegativity between hydrogen and fluorine than between hydrogen and iodine, as the iodine atom is so much bigger than that of fluorine (see page 135).

The ionic resonance energy of a bond A—B, then, is a measure of the difference in electronegativity between A and B. On this basis it is possible to allot to each element a number, such that the difference between any pair of numbers is directly related to the ionic resonance energy of the bond between the pair of elements concerned. Table 8 gives these electronegativity values for some elements in relation to their positions in the periodic table.

TABLE 8

ELECTRONEGATIVITY VALUES

			H 2·1			
Li 1·0	Be 1·5	B 2·0	C 2·5	N 3·0	O 3·5	F 4·0
Na 0·9	Mg 1·2	Al 1·5	Si 1·8	P 2·1	S 2·5	Cl 3·0
						Br 2·8
						I 2·5

The electronegativity value (x) of an element is such that $x_B - x_A$ is approximately equal to the square root of the ionic resonance energy of the bond $A—B$ measured in electron-volts (see page 23). This statement is illustrated below for the halides of hydrogen.

	H—F	H—Cl	H—Br	H—I
Ionic resonance energy in k.cal./gm. mol. . .	64·0	22·1	12·5	1·6
Ionic resonance energy in electron-volts (I) . .	2·77	0·96	0·54	0·069
$\sqrt{I}$	1·67	0·98	0·74	0·26
$x_B - x_A$	1·90	0·90	0·70	0·40

It is seen that the agreement between $x_B - x_A$ and the square root of the ionic resonance energy in electron-volts is only approximate, but compounds other than the hydrogen halides have to be considered, and the electronegativity values allotted have to be those which give the best agreement over a wide range of compounds. The difference between 0·26 and 0·40 in the case of hydrogen iodide is quite large, but for other compounds of hydrogen and iodine the electronegativity values give results in much closer agreement with the square root of the ionic resonance energy. This is shown in the following table:

	S—H	N—H	Si—I	As—I
$\sqrt{I}$.	0·41	0·98	0·71	0·57
$x_B - x_A$.	0·40	0·90	0·70	0·50

As the difference in the electronegativity values between an element A and an element B gives a measure of the ionic character of the bond A—B, it is possible to estimate the approximate percentage ionic character of a bond. The greater the difference $x_B - x_A$ the greater the ionic character of the bond A—B. An $x_B - x_A$ value of 1·7 leads to 50% ionic character; a value of 2·3 to 73%. These estimates of ionic character are, however, only approximate because of the difficulty of measuring the actual ionic character of any bond precisely.

9. Directed Covalent Bonds. That covalent bonds are directed in space is shown both by the existence of stereoisomerism in covalent compounds and by the actual measurement of the angles between covalent bonds. The atoms in a water molecule, for instance, are not in a straight line but are arranged as shown, and a similar angle is obtained for many other compounds containing three atoms.

$$O\begin{matrix} \diagup H \\ {\rangle}\ 104°\ 31' \\ \diagdown H \end{matrix}$$

This 'directed' nature of the covalent bond is explained in terms of the various orbits within an atom available for bond formation.

There is only one s orbit in any shell and this orbit is said to be 'spherically symmetrical'; this means that it is not concentrated in any particular direction. There are, however, three p orbits in a shell (see page 27) and these are visualised as being concentrated in different directions, mutually at right angles. This is illustrated in Fig. 19. Similarly each of the five d orbits and the seven f orbits in any shell are concentrated in different directions. It is this directional concentration of the p, d, and f orbits which results in the directional nature of the covalent bond.

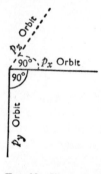

FIG. 19. Illustration of the directional arrangement of three p orbits

In the water molecule, the unpaired electrons taking part in the bond formation are in the s orbits for the hydrogen atom and in the p orbits of the oxygen atoms (see page 29). The hydrogen atoms can therefore form bonds in any direction but the oxygen atoms can only form bonds at right angles to each other. Thus two s—p bonds are formed and these would be expected to be at right angles to each other. That the observed value is greater than 90° is probably due to the partial ionic character of the O—H bond (see pages 86–91). This would give positive charges to the two hydrogen atoms in a water molecule and cause them to repel each other and increase the bond angle. For hydrogen sulphide, where the ionic character of the bond is not so great, the observed angle is 92° 20′.

In ammonia, involving three s—p bonds, it would be expected that the three bonds would be at right angles to each other. The actual bond angles are each 108° and the divergence from 90° is again probably due to the partial ionic character of the bonds. The arrangement of the bonds in ammonia is as shown in Fig. 20, the non-existence of optical isomers of substituted ammonias of the type Nabc being accounted for by the fact that the molecule can easily turn inside out.

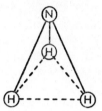

FIG. 20. Pyramidal arrangement of bonds in ammonia

10. Hybridisation of Bonds. Since p orbits are directionally concentrated, whereas s orbits are not, there is a difference in the strength of s—s, s—p, and p—p bonds. A quantitative treatment shows that the relative bond energies are

s—s	s—p	p—p
1	1·732	3

When carbon forms four covalent bonds three of its unpaired electrons are in p orbits whilst one is in an s orbit (see page 78). It might be expected that of the four bonds formed three would be at right angles to each other and stronger than the fourth.

This assumes that all the orbits retain their individuality, but theoretical calculations show that, by a combination of s and p orbits, four equivalent bonds, stronger than p—p bonds, can be formed, and that these bonds are directed towards the corners of a tetrahedron. This, of course, is in agreement with the idea of a tetrahedral arrangement of the four valency bonds of carbon, first suggested in 1874 by Le Bel and van't Hoff.

Bonds formed by the 'welding' together of two or more orbits are described as *hybrid bonds*, and the process of 'welding' is known as hybridization. In the case of carbon the four bonds are referred to as sp^3 bonds.

Elements in the first short period have only four incomplete orbits and are therefore limited to four covalent bonds (see page 76). In heavier atoms more than four covalent bonds are possible and d orbits may be used as well as s and p orbits. This introduces more possibilities of hybridisation, though the five d orbits are used less than the s and p orbits as they are less stable. In the transition elements, however, the d orbits in the penultimate shell have about the same energy level as the s and p orbits in the outer shell, and it is in these elements that hybridisation between s, p, and d orbits is of most importance.

The problem is capable of a detailed analysis in terms of the orbits available, hybridisation possibilities, and the number of unshared electrons, but a summary of the main results obtained must suffice here. Some of the types of bond which can be formed are shown below.

Number of bonds	Type of bond	Angular distribution of bond	Typical examples
1	s—s	Not directional	Hydrogen
2 3	s—p s—p	Mutually perpendicular	H_2O . H_2S . SO_2 . Cl_2O NH_3 . PCl_3
4	sp^3	Tetrahedral	CH_4 . CCl_4 . $SnCl_4$. $[Zn(NH_3)_4]^{++}$ $[Cu(CN)_4]^{---}$
4	dsp^2	Square	$[Cu(NH_3)_4]^{++}$.$[Ni(CN)_4]^{--}$.$[PtCl_4]^{--}$
6	d^2sp^3 or sp^3d^2 *	Octahedral	SF_6 . SeF_6 . $[Co(NH_3)_6]^{+++}$. $[Fe(CN)_6]^{--}$. $[Fe(CN)_6]^{---}$. $[PtCl_6]^{--}$

* d^2sp^3 indicates the use of two d orbits in the shell with principle quantum number one less than the shell containing the s and p orbits used. sp^3d^2 indicates that all the orbits used are in the same shell.

Other hybridization possibilities occur and give rise to further angular distributions of bonds. In many cases the theoretical distribution of bonds is in agreement with results previously suggested from a study of the various isomers which are known of the compounds concerned (see page 105). A study of magnetic properties also throws some light on the types of bond formed in some compounds; the matter is discussed on page 109.

11. Covalent Bonds in Crystals. Mention has already been made of the calcium carbonate crystal (see page 63); this is an ionic crystal made up of calcium ions and carbonate ions. Covalent bonds hold the carbonate ions together as an entity and in that way play some part in the formation of the crystal. Many metallic nitrates and sulphates are similar, too.

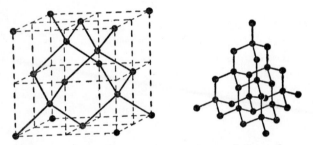

FIG. 21. Two views of the crystal structure of diamond

Other types of crystal occur, however, in which all the atoms in the crystal are held to each other by covalent bonds, and in which electrovalent bonds play no part. Such crystals are spoken of as *covalent lattices*; there are three main structures as follows.

(a) *The diamond structure (Fig. 21).* In a diamond crystal each carbon atom is surrounded by four other carbon atoms arranged tetrahedrally, the atoms being linked by covalent bonds. This 'interlocking' network of atoms accounts for the extreme hardness of diamond.

(b) *The zinc-blende structure (Fig. 22).* Zinc blende is one form of zinc sulphide. The crystal structure is related to that of diamond, the only difference being that adjacent atoms are different. Thus each zinc atom is surrounded by four sulphur atoms arranged tetrahedrally, and each sulphur atom by four zinc atoms similarly arranged.

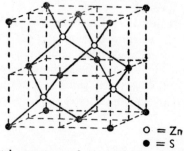

O = Zn
● = S

FIG. 22. Crystal structure of zinc blende. Compare the crystal structure of diamond shown in fig. 21

Other common substances which crystallise with the zinc-blende structure are cuprous chloride, cuprous bromide, cuprous iodide, aluminium phosphide, silicon carbide, and the sulphides of beryllium, cadmium, and mercury.

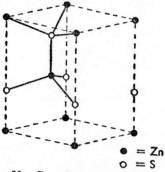

● = Zn
O = S

FIG. 23. Crystal structure of wurtzite

(c) *The wurtzite structure (Fig. 23).* Wurtzite is another form of zinc sulphide and the structure, as shown, is closely related to the zinc-blende structure.

Silver iodide, beryllium oxide, zinc oxide, cadmium sulphide, and aluminium nitride all form crystals with the wurtzite structure.

12. Layer Lattices. Graphite has a different structure from its allotrope, diamond. The crystal (Fig. 24) contains layers of hexagonally arranged carbon atoms, and, within the layers, the atoms are linked by covalent bonds. Adjacent layers, however, are held together by weak van der Waals' forces (see page 43) and they can slip over each other quite easily. This explains the soft, flaky nature of graphite.

A crystal structure such as this is known as a layer lattice

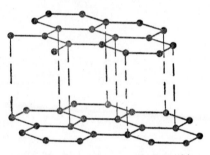

FIG. 24. Crystal structure of graphite

structure. In graphite, covalent bonds and van der Waals' forces are involved. In another large group of substances, however, layer lattices occur involving electrovalent bonds within the layers and van der Waals' forces between them.

In cadmium chloride, $CdCl_2$, for instance, each Cd^{++} ion is surrounded octahedrally by six Cl^- ions, but these $CdCl_6$ groups are linked together (each group sharing three Cl^- ions) into infinite layers. A two-dimensional representation is shown in Fig. 25, but the actual arrangement within the layer is three-dimensional. Such layers are held together within the crystal as a whole by van der Waals' forces.

Substances which crystallise with similar, or closely

related, structures include the dichlorides and dibromides of Mg, Cd, Fe, Co, and Ni, the diiodides of Ca, Cd, Fe, Co, and Ni, $CrCl_3$, $CrBr_3$, $FeCl_3$, SnS_2, and the dihydroxides of Mg, Ca, Cd, Mn, Fe, Co, and Ni.

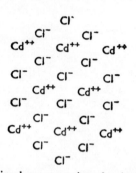

FIG. 25. Two-dimensional representation of a single layer in the layer lattice of cadmium chloride. In three dimensions all the Cd— ions are in one plane, with the Cl⁻ ions in alternate horizontal rows above or below this plane

In $Zn(OH)_2$, $Be(OH)_2$, $Al(OH)_3$, and $Fe(OH)_3$, the arrangement is similar but the various layers are held together by hydrogen bonds (see page 150) rather than by van der Waals' forces.

CHAPTER SEVEN

THE DATIVE BOND

1. Dipole Moments. The formation of a dative bond has already been described (page 38) and demands the donation of a pair of electrons by a donor to an acceptor; it is represented as $A \rightarrow B$, where A is the donor and B the acceptor. Both a covalent bond and a dative bond are made up of a pair of electrons shared between two atoms, and what has been said about covalent bonds in the last chapter applies, almost invariably, to dative bonds.

In the formation of a dative bond, however, there is a transfer of two electrons and hence of electric charge. For this reason the bond is sometimes written as $A^{\oplus}{-}B^{\ominus}$ instead of $A \rightarrow B$. The transfer of charge results in one of the atoms linked by a dative bond having a residual negative charge whilst the other has a residual positive charge, and this means that the bond has a permanent electrical dipole moment just as a magnet has a magnetic moment.

The existence of such a dipole moment in a bond does not necessarily mean that the bond is a dative one, for a normal covalent bond may have a dipole moment, if and when the shared pair of electrons which constitute the covalent bond are not shared evenly between the two atoms they unite. The dipole moment of a dative bond is, however, larger than that of most covalent bonds.

The measurement of dipole moments can often throw some light on the types of bond which exist in a molecule; the methods employed are outlined on page 127.

2. Co-ordination Compounds. Many compounds are known which seem to be made up of two perfectly stable molecules combined together for no apparent reason.

Potassium ferrocyanide, for instance, has a composition which can be represented by $K_4Fe(CN)_6$, and in the early days of structural chemistry the only structure which could be allotted to it was written as $Fe(CN)_2.4KCN$, i.e. it was regarded as a compound of potassium cyanide and ferrous cyanide, but what the dot signified in the structure as written was quite unknown.

That this structure is not at all satisfactory is shown by the fact that potassium ferrocyanide does not form either ferrous or cyanide ions in solution. Potassium ions are produced, however, and Werner suggested that the iron atom and the cyanide radicals were combined together to form what we now call a complex ion. The compound was then written as $K_4[Fe(CN)_6]$, the square bracket indicating that the group within it ionised as a whole, but the difficulty remained as to how the six cyanide radicals were attached to the central iron atom.

A large number of similar compounds exist and they were all formulated in the same way as potassium ferrocyanide. Some typical examples are

$K_3[Fe(CN)_6]$
Potassium ferricyanide

$[Cu(NH_3)_4]SO_4$
Cuprammonium sulphate

$K_3[Co(NO_2)_6]$
Potassium cobaltinitrite

$K_3[Cu(CN)_4]$
Potassium cuprocyanide

$[Co(NH_3)_6]Cl_3$
Hexamminocobaltic chloride

$(NH_4)_2[SnCl_6]$
Ammonium stannichloride

These complex compounds are always made up of a simple ion and a complex ion, both of which may be either anion or cation. The link between the complex and the simple ion is an electrovalent link, as in a simple salt. In the complex ion a number of groups are attached to a central metallic atom and the actual number of such groups was called by Werner the co-ordination number.[*] It is usually 2 or 4 or 6, but may be 8 or an odd number in rare cases.

The linkages within the complex ion must clearly be non-ionic as the complex remains intact in solution. If in the ferrocyanide ion, for instance, the linkages were ionic, it would be expected that it would split up in solution into ferrous and cyanide ions, but this does not occur. It was suggested that the groups were attached to the central atom by dative bonds, and that potassium ferrocyanide should be formulated as

$$K_4^+ \left\{ \begin{array}{c} CN \\ NC \searrow \downarrow \swarrow CN \\ Fe \\ NC \nearrow \uparrow \nwarrow CN \\ CN \end{array} \right\}^{= =}$$

The cyanide ion has a structure $(: C \equiv N :)^-$, and with lone pairs on both the carbon and nitrogen atoms it can clearly act as a donor. The charge on the ferrocyanide ion, as shown, results from a combination of six CN^- ions and one Fe^{++} ion. Potassium ferricyanide,

$$K_3^+ \left\{ \begin{array}{c} CN \\ NC \searrow \downarrow \swarrow CN \\ Fe \\ NC \nearrow \uparrow \nwarrow CN \\ CN \end{array} \right\}^{- -}$$

contains the ferricyanide ion with a smaller charge resulting from the combination of six CN^- ions and one Fe^{+++} ion.

A further example in which the complex ion is a cation is

[*] This use of the term co-ordination number must not be confused with the crystallographer's use of the term (see page 61).

provided by hexamminocobaltic chloride which is represented by

$$\left\{ \begin{array}{c} NH_3 \\ H_3N \searrow \downarrow \swarrow NH_3 \\ Co \\ H_3N \nearrow \uparrow \nwarrow NH_3 \\ NH_3 \end{array} \right\}^{+++} \quad Cl_3^{-}$$

Here the charge on the hexamminocobaltic ion is the same as that on the cobaltic ion, Co^{+++}, as the NH_3 coordinating groups are not charged.

The more detailed arrangement of electrons in a complex ion is discussed on page 108.

3. Metallic Ammines. The largest number of complex compounds involve ammonia as the co-ordinating group and are known as ammines; hexamminocobaltic chloride is a simple example. The compounds are not easy to prepare but interesting series can be obtained. With platinum, for instance, the following are known:

Name of complex	Formula	Charge on complex ion	Proportion of ionisable chlorine
Hexamminoplatinic chloride .	$[Pt(NH_3)_6]Cl_4$	+4	All
Monochloropentamminoplatinic chloride	$[Pt(NH_3)_5Cl]Cl_3$	+3	$\frac{3}{4}$
Dichlorotetramminoplatinic chloride	$[Pt(NH_3)_4Cl_2]Cl_2$	+2	$\frac{1}{2}$
Trichlorotriamminoplatinic chloride	$[Pt(NH_3)_3Cl_3]Cl$	+1	$\frac{1}{4}$
Tetrachlorodiamminoplatinic chloride	$Pt(NH_3)_2Cl_4$	0	None
Potassium pentachloroammino platinate	$[PtNH_3Cl_5]K$	−1	None
Potassium hexachloroplatinate .	$[PtCl_6]K_2$	−2	None

The main difference between the various compounds lies, of course, in the charge on the complex ion and in the proportion of ionisable chlorine, as shown in the table.

The structures of the second and sixth members of the series are given as

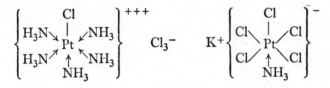

The series is formed by the replacement of ammonia molecules in the complex ion by charged chlorine ions, and, as we shall see, this type of replacement is a common feature of the chemistry of complex compounds.

4. Chelate Compounds. In the complex compounds considered so far, the groups attached to the central atoms have been attached by only one bond, but other groups exist which may be attached by two, three, or even four bonds. Such groups are called chelate groups, and the compounds formed, chelate compounds (from the Greek χηλή =a crab's claw).

A group capable of forming two links is called a bidentate group and an example is provided by ethylene diamine, $NH_2.CH_2.CH_2.NH_2$. The compounds

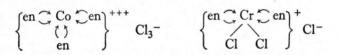

are typical.* Substances other than ethylene diamine which

* en is used to represent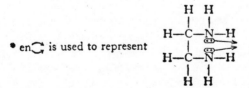

8

can behave in the same way are glycol, $HO.CH_2.CH_2.OH$, α, α′ -dipyridyl

and some ions such as the oxalate ion

$$\begin{bmatrix} COO \\ | \\ COO \end{bmatrix}^{--}$$

and the ion of glycine

$$CH_2.NH_2.COO^-$$

Typical tridentate groups are αβγ triamino propane,

$$\begin{array}{c} CH_2.NH_2 \\ | \\ CH.NH_2 \\ | \\ CH_2.NH_2 \end{array}$$

and tripyridyl

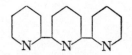

5. Geometrical Arrangement of Groups in Complex Ions.

A good deal of work has been done in an attempt to elucidate the geometrical arrangement of the various groups in complex compounds. Werner was able to make considerable progress by studying the isomeric forms which exist (see page 105), and in more recent years this work has been extended and enhanced by the use of X-rays and other modern methods. The results obtained are in agreement with the results predicted from a theoretical consideration of bond hybridisation (see page 93), and a square coplanar arrangement of complex ions of nickel was, in fact, predicted by Pauling and then proved experimentally.

As has been mentioned (page 101), the main co-ordination numbers are 4 and 6. The normal arrangement of 4 groups around a central atom is the tetrahedral arrangement as found, for instance, in carbon compounds. This arrangement occurs in most complex ions with 4 co-ordination, e.g. $[Zn(CN)_4]^{--}$, $[Zn(NH_3)_4]^{++}$, but in some cases the four groups are arranged at the corners of a square in a coplanar arrangement. This latter arrangement is found particularly with complex ions of Ni, Pt, and Pd, and of Cu, Ag, and Au. Some examples of square planar ions are $[PtCl_4]^{--}$, $[Ni(CN)_4]^{--}$, $[Cu(NH_3)_4]^{++}$, $[en \hspace{-0.3em} \diagdown \hspace{-0.3em} Pd \hspace{-0.3em} \diagdown \hspace{-0.3em} en]^{++}$, $[AuBr_4]^{-}$, but when the central metallic atom exhibits a different valency the complexes may be tetrahedral.

So far as complex ions with 6 co-ordination are concerned they are almost invariably octahedral. Examples are $[Co(NH_3)_6]^{+++}$, $[Fe(CN)_6]^{==}$, and $[PtCl_6]^{--}$.

6. Inorganic Isomerism. The existence of isomers of many co-ordination compounds shows that dative bonds must be fixed in space in the same way as covalent bonds (see page 91).

It was by a study of the various isomers which could be isolated that Werner was able to predict the geometrical arrangement of many complex ions. A 4-co-ordinated complex, Ma_2b_2, for instance, will exist in two isomeric forms if the arrangement is planar, but only one if it is tetrahedral. Similarly, a 6-co-ordinated complex, Ma_4b_2, will have two isomers if the arrangement is octahedral but three (corresponding to ortho, meta, and para substitution in organic chemistry) if it is planar and hexagonal. Thus an experimental determination of the number of isomers formed by a particular complex ion fixes the geometric arrangement within the ion.

The main types of inorganic isomerism may be summarised as follows.

(a) *Geometric isomerism.* This type of isomerism occurs in 6-co-ordinated complexes with an octahedral arrangement, and in 4-co-ordinated complexes with a planar arrangement. It does not occur in tetrahedral complexes.

Thus $[Co(NH_3)_4Cl_2]Cl$ exists in two forms represented as follows:

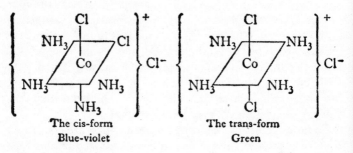

The cis-form	The trans-form
Blue-violet	Green

and many other Ma_4b_2 and Ma_3b_3 complex ions form similar isomers.

In planar (4-co-ordinated) complexes the two forms of Ma_2b_2 are represented as follows

The cis-form   The trans-form

e.g. $Pt(NH_3)_2Cl_2$.

(b) *Optical isomerism.* Optical isomerism arises, as in organic chemistry, when a compound can be represented by two asymmetrical structures one being the mirror image of the other. This occurs in many chelate compounds; for example, $[Co(en)_2Cl_2]Cl$ has optically active isomers represented by

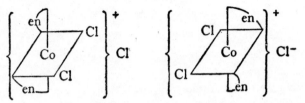

both of which are cis-forms, and also an inactive trans-form:

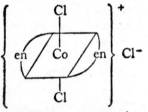

A similar example which does not contain any carbon atoms is provided by $[Rh(SO_2N_2H_2)_2(H_2O)_2]^-Na^+$ the cis-form of which is resolvable into optical isomers. The structures are:

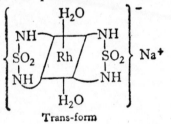

Trans-form

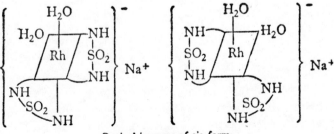

Optical isomers of cis-form

(c) *Ionisation isomerism.*   E.g.

[Co(NH₃)₅SO₄]Br

Sulphatopentamminocobaltic
bromide

[Co(NH₃)₅Br]SO₄

Bromopentamminocobaltic
sulphate

The first compound will give a precipitate with silver nitrate solution but not with barium chloride solution; the second compound will behave in the opposite way.

7. The Arrangement of Electrons in Complex Ions.

The suggestion that complex ions are held together by dative bonds has proved very useful.   It was originally thought that the central atom of the complex ion attained an inert gas structure, but whilst this is often so it is not an essential feature of complex ion formation.   Many stable complex ions are formed in which the central atom has not got an inert gas structure.

In the hexamminocobaltic ion the state of affairs is summarised as follows:

Number of electrons associated with cobalt atom $= 27$

Number of electrons associated with Co^{+++} ion $= 24$

Number of electrons associated with the cobalt
atom in $[Co(NH_3)_6]^{+++}$, the six ammonia
molecules each providing two electrons $= 36$

In this example the cobalt atom has attained an inert gas number (krypton).

In the ferricyanide ion, however, the arrangement is as follows, and there is no inert gas structure:

Number of electrons associated with iron atom $= 26$

Number of electrons associated with Fe^{+++} ion $= 23$

Number of electrons associated with iron atom
in $[Fe(CN)_6]^{---}$ ion $= 35$

The attainment of a stable geometrical arrangement seems to be as important as the attainment of an inert gas structure.

When an inert gas structure is not found in a complex ion there is normally a deficiency of electrons rather than an excess, and the latter must be unstable. The complex ion $[Co(CN)_6]^{==}$, for instance, is unstable; it would demand an arrangement of 37 electrons around the cobalt atom.

Whatever the electronic arrangement which leads to stability in complex compounds many of them are remarkably stable. Moreover, the formation of a complex ion often stabilises an otherwise unstable ion. Cupric iodide, for example, is unstable but the complex compound

$$[en \leftrightharpoons Cu \rightleftharpoons en]I_2$$

is stable, and, whereas ferrous salts are readily oxidised on exposure to air, the complex compounds *

$$\left\{ \begin{array}{c} \text{dipy} \leftrightharpoons \text{Fe} \rightleftharpoons \text{dipy} \\ (\ ) \\ \text{dipy} \end{array} \right\} X_2$$

are quite stable.

A good deal of information as to the arrangement of electrons in complex ions is provided by magnetic measurements and a brief outline of the results obtained is given in the next section.

8. Magnetic Evidence. It is explained on page 68 that an ion which contains n unpaired electrons has a magnetic moment of $\sqrt{n(n+2)}$ Bohr magnetons, and that the value of n can be discovered by measuring the actual moment.

The structure of the Fe^{++} ion, for instance, is shown below at (a):

	1s	2s	2p	3s	3p	3d	4s	4p
(a) Fe++	2	2	222	2	222	21111		
(b)	2	2	222	2	222	222		
(c) [Fe(CN)6]==	2	2	222	2	222	222 22	2	222

* dipy is used as an abbreviation for the dipyridyl group (see page 104).

There are four unpaired electrons and the expected magnetic moment of compounds containing this ion would be 4·90 (see Fig. 16, page 68); the measured moment of hydrated ferrous sulphate is, in fact, 5·25. In forming the ferrocyanide ion, $[Fe(CN)_6]^{==}$, the electrons in the Fe^{++} ion probably rearrange, however, until they are all paired as in (b). This now leaves two $3d$ orbits vacant, and together with the vacant $4s$ and $4p$ orbits, six d^2sp^3 (see page 94) bonds can be formed to give rise to the octahedral complex ion in which the electronic arrangement would be as in (c), the bonding electrons being enclosed in the rectangle. All the electrons in (c) are paired and it would be expected that the ferrocyanide ion would be diamagnetic; this is found to be so.

In forming the ferricyanide ion the position is slightly different. The electronic arrangement in the Fe^{+++} ion is as shown below, (a):

		1s	2s	2p	3s	3p	3d	4s	4p
(a)	Fe^{+++}	2	2	222	2	222	11111		
(b)		2	2	222	2	222	221		
(c)	$[Fe(CN)_6]^{--}$	2	2	222	2	222	221	22	2	222

There are now five unpaired electrons, and the calculated magnetic moment for ferric compounds of 5·92 corresponds with measured values of 5·86 for ferric sulphate. Prior to bond formation the electrons rearrange as at (b), and the six bonds then form as d^2sp^3 bonds as in the previous example. The resulting electronic arrangement is shown in (c) and it will be noticed that one of the $3d$ electrons is unpaired. This should lead to a magnetic moment of 1·73 magnetons and the observed value is near to this.

Both the ferrocyanide and the ferricyanide ions involve the formation of d^2sp^3 bonds and are octahedral (see page 94). In the formation of $[Ni(CN)_4]^{--}$, however, such bonds are not possible because there are not two d orbits vacant. The electronic structure for the Ni^{++} ion is shown below, (a), and if the electrons regroup as in (b) before

	1s	2s	2p	3s	3p	3d	4s	4p
(a) Ni^{++}	2	2	222	2	222	22211		
(b)	2	2	222	2	222	2222		
(c) $[Ni(CN)_4]^{--}$	2	2	222	2	222	2222⎡2	2	22⎤
(d) $[Cu(NH_3)_4]^{++}$	2	2	222	2	222	2222⎡2	2	22⎤1
(e) Cu^+	2	2	222	2	222	22222		
(f) $[Cu(CN)_4]^{--}$	2	2	222	2	222	22222	⎡2	222⎤

combination there is only one vacant d orbit. The four bonds formed will, therefore, be dsp^2 bonds leading to an electronic structure as in (c). Such bonds result in a square coplanar complex (see page 94), and as all the electrons are paired it is diamagnetic. In the corresponding planar complex, $[Cu(NH_3)_4]^{++}$, the final state of affairs is shown in (d), and as there is one unpaired electron the complex is paramagnetic; the calculated moment is 1·73 and the observed value in cuprammonium sulphate is 1·82.

In $[Cu(CN)_4]^{--}$ neither d^2sp^3 nor dsp^2 bonds can be formed for the arrangement of electrons in the Cu^+ ion is as in (e) and there are no vacant d orbits. Four sp^3 bonds are, therefore, formed leading to a tetrahedral arrangement; as all the electrons are paired the complex is diamagnetic.

9. Hydration of Ions. The suggestion that ions are hydrated in solution has already been introduced (page 66) and there is plenty of varied evidence to support this. The presence of water of crystallisation in solid hydrated salts suggests, too, that ions may be hydrated in the solid state.

Although all the numerous cases which are known have not by any means been fully explained, hydrated ions must be regarded as complex ions, but the bonds may not be pure dative bonds.

The water molecule has two lone pairs on the oxygen

atom and is quite capable of acting as a donor and forming dative bonds. The molecule has, however, a large electric dipole moment (see page 127), the covalent bonds having considerable ionic character.* It behaves in fact in many ways as though its structure was

$$O^{--} \begin{array}{l} H^+ \\ \\ H^+ \end{array}$$

and the linkage between a metallic ion and water in a complex ion may be due to electrostatic attraction between the positively charged metallic ion and the negatively charged oxygen atom in the water molecule.

The type of linkage in a complex ion containing water may, therefore, be considered either as a dative bond or as an electrostatic attraction. By analogy with the ammines and other complex ions it would be expected that the links would be dative bonds. Magnetic evidence, however, favours the electrostatic binding in certain tested substances. The observed magnetic moment of solid hydrated ferrous sulphate, for instance, is 5·25, and this corresponds to the presence of four unpaired electrons in the Fe^{++} ion (see (a), below). If water molecules were attached to the Fe^{++} ion by dative bonds, there would not be four unpaired electrons, and the magnetic moment would not be 5·25. The $[Fe(CN)_6]^{=-}$ ion, for example, has six cyanide ions linked to the central Fe^{++} ion by six d^2sp^3 bonds as in (b), and this arrangement leaves no unpaired electrons so that the magnetic moment is zero:

		$1s$	$2s$	$2p$	$3s$	$3p$	$3d$	$4s$	$4p$
(a)	Fe^{++}	2	2	222	2	222	21111		
(b)	$[Fe(CN)_6]^{-=-}$	2	2	222	2	222	222	22 2	222

* The difference in the electronegativity values of oxygen and hydrogen is 1·4 and this corresponds to a bond between the two atoms having 39% ionic character (see page 91).

So far as the actual number of molecules of water associated with any ions is concerned, it is difficult to make any generalisations for the number of known hydrates is so large and varied.

Sidgwick regarded the links in a hydrated ion as dative bonds and applied Fajans' rules to the problem (see page 51). These rules state that an ion will have a greater tendency to be hydrated (*a*) the greater the charge on the ion, (*b*) the greater the size of the ion, if an anion, and (*c*) the smaller the size of an ion, if a cation, for these are the conditions favouring covalent bond formation. Even though the bonds may not be dative bonds the general conclusions arrived at by Sidgwick still fit the facts.

For a cation, high charge and small size should lead to hydration, and considering the charge, it is true that, whereas most univalent ions are not hydrated those exhibiting a higher valency are. The effect of the size of the cation is well shown in the alkali series. Lithium is the smallest of the alkali metal atoms and all lithium salts are hydrated. Many sodium salts are hydrated, some potassium salts are, but salts of rubidium and caesium are invariably anhydrous. Moreover, the Li^+ ion with the smallest size would be expected to have the highest mobility whereas it is found to have the lowest; this is because it must be regarded not as a simple ion but as a hydrated ion and the hydration increases its effective size.

The geometric arrangement of the water molecules in hydrated salts is similar to that in ammines. Salt hydrates have the general formula $M_xA_y.zH_2O$, and where z is 4 or 6 the water molecules are arranged tetrahedrally or octahedrally. This is shown by examination of the crystal structure of solids, but the arrangement probably holds in solution, too. Some examples of hydrates with co-ordination numbers 4 or 6 are given at the top of the following page.

$BeSO_4.4H_2O$　　　　　　　$MgCl_2.6H_2O$
$BeCO_3.4H_2O$　　　　　　　$AlCl_3.6H_2O$
　　　　　　　　　　　　　　$NiSO_4.6H_2O$
　　　　　　　　　　　　　　$Fe(NO_3)_2.6H_2O$
　　　　　　　　　　　　　　$FeCl_3.6H_2O$

Where the value of z in $M_xA_y.zH_2O$ is not 4 or 6 the position is not quite so simple. When z is less than the normal co-ordination number of the metal, M, the metal is surrounded in the crystal both by water molecules and acid radical groups, A. When z is greater than the normal co-ordination number it was at first thought that the extra water molecules formed complex ions with the anion in the salt. $CuSO_4.5H_2O$, for instance, was regarded as

$$[Cu(H_2O)_4]^{++}[SO_4(H_2O)]^{--}$$

and $NiSO_4.7H_2O$ as $[Ni(H_2O)_6]^{++}[SO_4(H_2O)]^{--}$, the complex anions containing hydrogen bonds (see page 150) as indicated below:

This view is now thought to be incorrect though hydrogen bonds (see page 150) are envisaged as holding the odd water molecules in the crystal between the complex ions and the acid radical ions. In solution the $[Cu(H_2O)_4]^{++}$ and $[Ni(H_2O)_6]^{++}$ ions are formed.

Examples in which z has a very large value, such as $MgCl_2.12H_2O$, $KAl(SO_4)_2.12H_2O$, $Na_2CO_3.10H_2O$, $Sr(OH)_2.8H_2O$, and $MgCl_2.8H_2O$, have not been fully investigated, but it may be significant that the numbers 8 and 12 (twice the more usual co-ordination numbers of 4 and 6) frequently recur. Both Werner and Sidgwick suggested that, in these cases, two water molecules occupied one co-ordination position, but this idea is not substantiated by X-ray crystallographic results.   In general, it is found that 4 or 6 of the molecules of water are closely associated with the central metallic atom as in a more normal hydrated salt, and that the remaining molecules are loosely held within the crystal.   Such water is referred to as *lattice water*; it must be present in the hydrates of methane and the inert gases.

CHAPTER EIGHT

EXPERIMENTAL METHODS

1. Summary of Methods. Many of the statements made in the preceding chapters may appear to be based on a theoretical rather than an experimental approach, but, whilst many of the important results already mentioned have followed from theoretical reasoning, the results are fully supported by reliable experimental measurements. In fact, as always in the development of science, it has been the failure of existing theories to account for newly discovered experimental results which has led to the postulation of newer theories.

The contributions made by a study of stereochemistry (page 105), by magnetic measurements (pages 66, 109), and by thermochemical experiments (page 82) have already been mentioned, but information as to the nature of valency bonds in molecules has come mainly from a study of molecular structure.

In investigating the structure of molecules the main methods may be summarised under the following headings:

    (*a*) Diffraction of X-rays,
    (*b*) Diffraction of electrons,
    (*c*) Spectroscopic methods, and
    (*d*) Measurement of dipole moments.

The principles underlying these various methods are outlined in the following sections, but it is not possible to go into the details of the experimental procedures. Some of the main features of the experimental results obtained are discussed in Chapter 9, and are, of course, referred to throughout the book.

DIFFRACTION OF X-RAYS

2. Diffraction of Light. If the sun is viewed through the fabric of an umbrella or a closely woven handkerchief, a pattern of spectra will be seen, and this effect is caused by what is known as diffraction. The phenomenon can be studied more precisely by using a diffraction grating, which consists of a large number of very fine opaque lines, parallel and of equal width, drawn on a piece of glass. When a beam of light is passed through such a grating the light is diffracted and, under the right conditions, a series of spectra can be observed on either side of the original path of light. If monochromatic light is used the spectra are replaced by a series of bright images on a dark background.

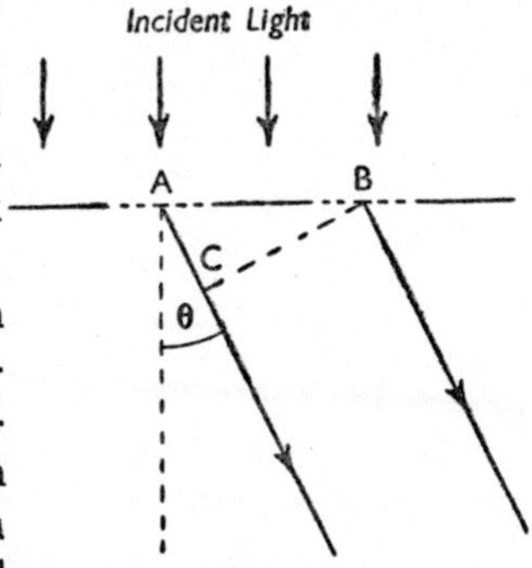

Fig. 26

A portion of the grating can be represented diagrammatically as in Fig. 26. If monochromatic light of wave-length λ is incident perpendicularly on the upper face of the grating all the clear spaces act as secondary sources of light and emit rays in all directions. The rays in any one direction from each of the spaces will interfere with each other. In simple terms, where a crest of one wave coincides with a crest of another the resulting displacement will be increased, i.e. the light will appear brighter. Similarly, when a crest of one wave coincides with a trough in another there will be a resultant displacement of zero, i.e. there will be no light visible.

The condition leading to a maximum displacement (reinforcement of rays) is illustrated at the top of the following page,

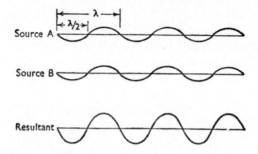

and that leading to a resultant displacement of zero (neutral-isation of rays) below,

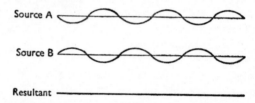

By considering the rays emitted at an angle θ with the normal to the grating, and by dealing with a resultant ray from the mid-point of each space, it is possible to treat the interference of the waves quantitatively as follows.

The ray from A will reinforce the ray from B to cause a maximum displacement only if the distance AC is equal to $n \cdot \lambda$, where n has any integral value. Now AC is equal to $AB \cdot \sin \theta$, and it follows that, for reinforcement, $AB \cdot \sin \theta$ must equal $n \cdot \lambda$, i.e.

$$d \cdot \sin \theta = n \cdot \lambda$$

where d is equal to AB.

If the grating has 14,000 lines to the inch then AB (d) is equal to 1/14,000th of an inch or, approximately, $1 \cdot 81 \times 10^{-4}$ cm. And if the wave-length of the light used is $5 \cdot 8 \times 10^{-5}$ cm. (yellow light) then $\sin \theta = 0 \cdot 3197 \cdot n$, the values of θ given by $n=0$, ±1, ±2, and ±3 being $0°$, $\pm18°\ 39'$, $\pm39°\ 45'$, and $\pm73°\ 33'$ respectively.

If then the light coming from such a grating is viewed

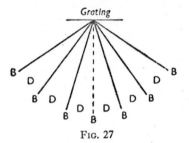

Fig. 27

through a movable telescope, a series of bright and dark lines will be seen as shown in Fig. 27, where bright lines are indicated by B and dark lines by D.

3. Diffraction of X-rays. The simple formula developed in the preceding section leads to two important experimental possibilities. By actually measuring the various values of θ which lead to the formation of bright lines, it is possible either to obtain a value of λ, if d is known, or to obtain a value of d, if λ is known.

In 1912, Laue suggested that if X-rays were electromagnetic waves of short wave-length, they should be diffracted in the same way as light waves, provided a diffraction grating with suitable spacing could be found. A crystal with a regular array of atoms in various planes was considered to be capable of acting as such a grating, and Friedrich and Knipping found that this was so. They passed a beam of X-rays through a thin section of a zinc blende crystal, and on photographing the emergent rays they found that the photographic plate showed a bright central spot surrounded symmetrically by other bright spots caused by diffraction of the X-rays.

The extension of this experimental result is obvious, for it

9

is only necessary to measure the relative positions of the bright spots formed, to use X-rays of known wave-length, and then, by applying the relationship $d . \sin \theta = n . \lambda$, to calculate the value of d, i.e. the internal dimensions of a crystal. This is, of course, a simplified statement of the problem, for the arrangement of atoms in a crystal is in three dimensions and the interpretation of the experimental results is in many cases far from easy, but the principle of the method should be clear.

4. Diffraction by Reflection. It is neither possible nor necessary to go very fully into the actual methods employed

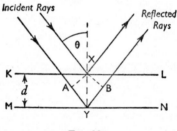

Fig. 28

in the X-ray analysis of a crystal. Mention must be made, however, of the fact that, whereas in the preceding sections we have been considering the diffraction of transmitted light or X-rays, the modern practical methods employed depend almost entirely on the diffraction of reflected X-rays, since the results obtained in this way are more easily interpreted.

The nature of diffraction by reflection is easily understood. The atoms in a crystal are arranged in a series of planes and the lines KL and MN in Fig. 28 may be taken as representing two such planes. When a beam of X-rays is incident on a crystal, some reflection takes place at each plane, and diffraction is caused by the interference of the reflected X-rays.

If X-rays at an angle of incidence, θ, are considered, the path difference between the reflection from the upper surface and that from the lower surface is equal to AYB. Taking the distance between the two planes as d, it follows that AY is equal to $d \cdot \cos \theta$, and AYB to $2d \cdot \cos \theta$. For the reflected rays to reinforce and form a bright image the necessary condition is that $2d \cdot \cos \theta$ must equal $n \cdot \lambda$ where n is any integer and λ is the wave-length of the incident X-rays.

By measurement of the various values of θ which lead to the formation of bright images by reflection, values of d can be obtained. The problem is, however, complicated by the presence in a crystal of atoms in more than one set of parallel

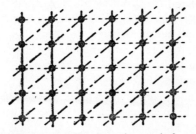

Fig. 29.   Some of the parallel planes in a typical crystal structure

planes. A crystal structure represented by Fig. 29, for instance, has, amongst others, the three sets of parallel planes shown. In interpreting the experimental data, however, some assistance is obtained from the fact that a plane which is thickly populated with ions or atoms is much more effective in reflecting X-rays than one in which the atoms or ions are more widely spaced.

DIFFRACTION OF ELECTRONS

5. Outline of Method. Practical methods of X-ray analysis of crystals have developed so rapidly since 1912 that these methods provide the greatest amount of information on the internal dimensions of crystals. The methods have been adopted, too, in the investigation of the internal structures of amorphous solids, liquids, glasses, fibres, vapours, and gases, and have given valuable results, but the problems involved are less simple than those in dealing with a solid crystal.

In a gas, for instance, the molecules have no fixed position in relation to each other. Nevertheless, if a beam of X-rays is incident on a gas, the scattering is such as to cause a diffraction pattern, and from such a pattern, which can be photographed, the interatomic distances in the gas molecule can be calculated.

So far as X-rays are concerned the method is theoretically sound and practically possible, but, because of the comparatively small number of gas molecules orientated correctly, the scattering power is low and long exposures are necessary. This drawback is overcome by the use of a stream of electrons instead of X-rays. It has been mentioned on page 29 that a stream of electrons behaves like a wave-like radiation, and can therefore be diffracted. By using such a stream of electrons long exposures are unnecessary, as gas molecules scatter electrons much more effectively than X-rays, and the scattered electrons affect a photographic plate more strongly.

The practical procedure is much the same whether X-rays or electrons are used. In either case interatomic distances and angles can be measured, and as there is no interaction between the molecules in a gas, such as there is between the ions in a crystal, the measurements are made on molecules in their normal state.

The same type of electron diffraction can be applied in investigating solid crystals and the results obtained agree with the X-ray results. A beam of electrons is, however, far less penetrating than a beam of X-rays, so that electron diffraction is only really suitable for investigating the surface structure of solids.   In general, diffraction of X-rays is used for crystals, and diffraction of electrons for gases and vapours.

6. Molecular Spectra.   Spectra provide an increasingly great amount of information as to the energy changes which can take place within an atom or a molecule, as any line in a spectrum corresponds either to an emission of energy or to an absorption.   The part played by a study of atomic spectra in the development of ideas of atomic structure has been described in Chapter 3.   The lines in such a spectrum come about as a result of the change of electrons in an atom between various orbits with different energy levels.

When a molecule is considered there are further possibilities of energy changes, and as a result molecular spectra are more complex than atomic spectra, consisting, in general, of groups of lines collected together in what are known as bands.   Such spectra are often referred to as *band spectra*, and may be further classified as to whether they are studied in the ultra-violet, visible, or infra-red regions.

The simplest treatment is concerned solely with diatomic molecules.   In such a molecule, energy changes may take place by virtue of an electronic change, or a vibrational change, or a rotational change, and the quantum theory idea, that energy can only be emitted or absorbed in small whole number multiples of some unit of energy (see page 16), applies to all three changes.

The values of the unit of energy (quanta) involved are, however, very different and are such that electronic changes lead to spectral lines in the visible and ultra-violet region of the spectrum, vibrational changes to lines in the near infrared, and rotational changes to lines in the near and far infrared.   An idea of the changes which can take place is given by Fig. 30.   A change from an energy level A to a level B follows from an electronic change, one from A to C from a vibrational change, and one from A to D from a rotational change. There are, of course, other similar changes of each type which may occur too.

In general the change in energy when a molecule passes

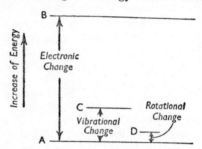

FIG. 30.　Types of energy change which can take place within a molecule

from a state 1 to a state 2 (indicated by superscripts) is given by E where

$$E = (E^1_{El} - E^2_{El}) + (E^1_{Vib} - E^2_{Vib}) + (E^1_{Rot} - E^2_{Rot}).$$

If there is no electronic change then

$$E = (E^1_{Vib} - E^2_{Vib}) + (E^1_{Rot} - E^2_{Rot}).$$

and if no electronic and no vibrational change

$$E = (E^1_{Rot} - E^2_{Rot}).$$

7. Interpretation of Molecular Spectra. (a) Rotational spectra.

The lines in the far infra-red of a molecular spectrum are due to rotational changes and are most easily interpreted to give information as to the dimensions of the molecules concerned. For a diatomic molecule made up of two atoms of masses m_1 and m_2, at a distance d apart, the moment of inertia for rotation about an axis perpendicular to the line joining the nuclei of the two atoms is given by $I = \dfrac{m_1 \cdot m_2}{m_1 + m_2} \cdot d^2$. If the angular velocity is ω, the kinetic energy of rotation is $\frac{1}{2} I \cdot \omega^2$, i.e. $\dfrac{m_1 \cdot m_2}{m_1 + m_2} \cdot \dfrac{d^2 \cdot \omega^2}{2}$.

Now, on the quantum theory, changes in the kinetic energy of the system can only take place in definite steps, and the possible energy changes are controlled by the fact that the angular momentum must be equal to $\dfrac{\sqrt{j(j+1)}\cdot h}{2\pi}$, where j is a whole number known as the rotational quantum number. The kinetic energy of the molecule can, therefore, have any value of $\dfrac{j(j+1)\cdot h^2}{8\pi^2\cdot I}$, j having whole number values.

When the value of j changes by 1, a quantum of radiation of frequency ν is emitted or absorbed such that

$$h\cdot\nu=\frac{h^2}{8\pi^2 I}\{(j+1)(j+2)-j(j+1)\}, \quad \text{i.e.} \quad \nu=\frac{h}{8\pi^2 I}(2j+2).$$

The frequencies of adjacent lines in the rotational spectrum of a molecule corresponding to $j=1$ and $j=2$ will therefore be $\dfrac{4h}{8\pi^2 I}$ and $\dfrac{6h}{8\pi^2 I}$, the difference between the two lines being $\dfrac{h}{4\pi^2 I}$.

This difference can be measured experimentally and in this way I and hence the interatomic distance d can be found.

(b) *Vibration-rotation spectra.* If a molecular spectrum is investigated in the near infra-red, the lines observed are formed both by vibrational and rotational changes. For each line corresponding to a vibrational change there is a series of lines related to the associated rotational changes. This is illustrated in Fig. 31. The distance between two rotational lines in this type of spectrum can be measured and is related to the interatomic distance in a way very similar to that described in (a) above.

(c) *Electronic-vibration-rotation spectra.* If a molecular spectrum is viewed in the ultra-violet or visible region the main lines are caused by electronic changes, and each of these lines has associated with it a fine structure due to vibrational changes, and a fine structure due to rotational changes. The complete spectrum is complicated, particularly as various

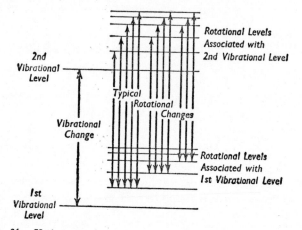

FIG. 31.   Various rotational changes associated with a vibrational change

bands may overlap. It is, however, possible to make measurements and obtain information in much the same way as in (*b*).

The vibration-rotation spectrum (*b*) yields, in general, the best results so far as the dimensions of a molecule are concerned. The spectra can be observed accurately and, for diatomic molecules the interpretation is reasonably straightforward. Electron-vibration-rotation spectra give results not obtainable by other methods but they are very difficult to interpret. Rotational spectra (*a*) are the simplest type but it has not been easy, until recently, to work in the far infra-red region, and, moreover, many of the results obtainable from this type of spectrum can be obtained from the vibration-rotation spectra.

DIPOLE MOMENTS

9. What is a Dipole Moment? A magnet has a magnetic moment given by $m \cdot l$, where m is the pole strength of the magnet and l the distance between the poles. In a similar way, if two equal and opposite electrical charges are separated, they constitute an electrical dipole moment, measured by the charge multiplied by the distance between the charges.

In an isolated atom, consisting of a positively charged nucleus surrounded by negatively charged electrons, the centres of action of both the positive and negative charge coincide and the atom does not possess a dipole moment; it is said to be *non-polar*. In a diatomic molecule, however, there may be a definite dipole moment. Thus, if two electrons involved in a covalent bond are not shared equally between the two atoms they unite, the bond will have a dipole moment, the atom which has the larger share in the electron pair being the negative end of the dipole. Similarly, when two atoms are linked by a dative bond there will always be polarity, the donor having a positive charge and the acceptor a negative one (see page 99).

Dipole moments are expressed in terms of e.s.u. or the Debye unit, one debye being equal to a dipole moment of 1×10^{-18} e.s.u. All dipole moments are of the order of 10^{-18} e.s.u. and this is to be expected for the charge on an electron is $4 \cdot 8025 \times 10^{-10}$ e.s.u. and molecular distances are of the order of 10^{-8}. Some typical values of dipole moments are given below in debyes:

Hydrogen fluoride	1·91
Hydrogen chloride	1·03
Hydrogen bromide	0·78
Hydrogen iodide	0·38
Water	1·80
Ammonia	1·57

The values for the hydrogen halides are those that would be expected, for as fluorine has the highest electronegativity value it has the greatest attraction for electrons (see page 89).

10. Measurement of Dipole Moments. The measurement of dipole moments depends largely on the determination of di-electric constants. The capacity of a condenser made up of two charged plates in vacuo is given by the expression $C = Q/V$, where Q is the charge on the plates and V the potential difference between them. If some material is placed between the two plates, the molecules of the material become electrically polarised by induction, and in this way give rise to a field which tends to neutralise that already existing between the plates. This leads to a decrease in the potential difference between the plates or, in other words, to an increase in the capacity of the condenser.

A material used in such a way is known as a di-electric and in general the capacity of a condenser is given by $C = \epsilon \cdot Q/V$ where ϵ is the dielectric constant of the material between the plates of the condenser. Typical numerical values of ϵ are 1 (or more accurately 1·000583) for air and 79·45 for water (see, also, page 66).

When a non-polar dielectric is placed between the plates of a condenser it becomes polarised in two ways. In the first place the negative electrons in the molecule of the dielectric are displaced with respect to the positive nuclei towards the positive plate of the condenser; this is known as *electronic polarisation*, P_E. Secondly, the nuclei may be displaced with respect to each other; this is called *atomic polarisation*, P_A.

If a polar molecule is considered, both electronic and atomic polarisation occur, but the molecule is also orientated along the direction of the lines of force between the plates of the condenser. This effect is known as *orientation polarisation*, P_O. In a polar molecule, then, the total polarisation, P, is equal to $P_E + P_A + P_O$, but it is only P_O

which bears any relation to the original dipole moment of the dielectric.

To obtain values for the dipole moment, then, it is a matter of measuring the total polarisation, P, and finding, if possible, the contribution made by orientation polarisation, P_O.

The total polarisation can be obtained by measuring the dielectric constant of the substance concerned, as the two are related by the Clausius–Mosotti law which states that

$$P = \frac{\epsilon - 1}{\epsilon + 2} \cdot \frac{M}{D}$$

where D is the density of the substance and M its molecular weight. To obtain values of P_O from P demands making measurements at different temperatures, for P_O varies with temperature whereas P_E and P_A are independent of temperature.

Once the value of P_O has been determined the value of the dipole moment can be obtained from it since

$$P_O = \frac{4\pi N}{3} \cdot \frac{\mu^2}{3kT}$$

where μ is the dipole moment, N the Avogadro number, T the absolute temperature, and k the Boltzmann constant.

Though the method outlined is the main method adopted in measuring dipole moments, other methods are available but cannot be discussed here.

CHAPTER NINE

INTERNAL DIMENSIONS OF CRYSTALS AND MOLECULES

1. Ionic Radii. X-ray analysis of crystals, and other methods, give values for the equilibrium distance between two ions in an ionic crystal. These values are, of course, very small and they are usually expressed in Angstrom units, 1 Angstrom unit (1A) being equal to 10^{-8} cm.

The internuclear distances for the halides of sodium and potassium are given in Table 9.

TABLE 9
INTERNUCLEAR DISTANCES FOR HALIDES OF SODIUM AND POTASSIUM

(Values in Angstrom units)

	K^+F^- 2·66	K^+Cl^- 3·14	K^+Br^- 3·29	K^+I^- 3·53
	Na^+F^- 2·31	Na^+Cl^- 2·81	Na^+Br^- 2·98	Na^+I^- 3·23
Difference	0·35	0·33	0·31	0·30

If the ions in a crystal are regarded as spheres the internuclear distance between two ions is made up of the sum of the ionic radii of the two ions (Fig. 32). Moreover, the constancy of the difference between the internuclear distances of sodium and potassium halides, as shown, indicates that in a series of such compounds the ionic radii of the anion and cation must be reasonably constant.

The actual internuclear distance does not give a value for an ionic radius, however, until any one ionic radius is decided by some other method. Goldschmidt, who did most of the early work in this field, took the radius of the fluoride ion as 1·33A and the oxygen ion as 1·32A, but Pauling has adopted the values of 1·36A and 1·40A for these ions, and the latter values are used in what follows.

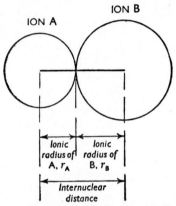

FIG. 32. The meaning of ionic radius

If the internuclear distance in NaF is 2·31A and the ionic radius of the F^- ion is 1·36A the ionic radius of the Na^+ ion must be 0·95A. In this way values for the ionic radii of all ions can be obtained, and a selection of the results is given in Table 10.

TABLE 10

Ionic Radii

(Values in Angstrom units)

Li^+ 0·60 Na^+ 0·95		Be^{++} 0·31 Mg^{++} 0·65		Al^{+++} 0·50			
K^+ 1·33	Cu^+ 0·96	Ca^{++} 0·99	Zn^{++} 0·74	Sc^{+++} 0·81	Ga^{+++} 0·62	Ti^{++++} 0·68	
Rb^+ 1·48	Ag^+ 1·26	Sr^{++} 1·13	Cd^{++} 0·97	Y^{+++} 0·93	In^{+++} 0·81	Zr^{++++} 0·80	Sn^{++++} 0·71
Cs^+ 1·69	Au^+ 1·37	Ba^{++} 1·35	Hg^{++} 1·10	La^{+++} 1·15	Tl^{+++} 0·95		Pb^{++++} 0·84

F^- 1·36	Cl^- 1·81	Br^- 1·95	I^- 2·16
O^- 1·40	S^- 1·84	Se^- 1·98	Te^- 2·21

A study of the numerical values given leads to the following pertinent conclusions, most of which simply serve to illustrate, numerically, general effects which have already been described:

(a) The ions of elements in any one group of the periodic table increase in size as the atomic weight of the element increases.

(b) For a series of ions with the same arrangement of extra-nuclear electrons the size of the ion decreases as the nuclear charge, i.e. the atomic number, increases, for, as the nuclear charge increases, the electrons are attracted more strongly and drawn inwards. This effect is observable in the series $O^=$, F^-, Na^+, Mg^{++}, Al^{+++} (all with a 2.8 structure), $S^=$, Cl^-, K^+, Ca^{++}, Sc^{+++} (all with a 2.8.8 structure), or Cu^+, Zn^{++}, Ga^{+++} (all with a 2.8.18 structure).

(c) When an element forms two positively charged ions the ion with the lower charge is larger than the more highly charged ion. This effect is to be expected for the ion with the higher charge has fewer extra-nuclear electrons than the ion of lower charge. Thus:

Tl^+ 1·44	Pb^{++} 1·21	Mn^{++} 0·80	Fe^{++} 0·75
Tl^{+++} 0·95	Pb^{++++} 0·84	Mn^{+++} 0·62	Fe^{+++} 0·60

(d) As compared with the size of an atom the corresponding cation is smaller whilst the anion is larger. This is again to be expected, for a positively charged ion is formed by the loss of electrons, those remaining being more strongly attracted by the nucleus, whilst a negatively charged ion is formed by a gain in the number of electrons and a resulting smaller nuclear attraction.   The following figures illustrate the general effect.

S atom, 1·04	O atom, 0·66	F atom, 0·64
S⁼ ion, 1·84	O⁼ ion, 1·40	F⁻ ion, 1·36
Fe atom, 1·35	Na atom, 1·54	Cl atom, 0·99
Fe⁺⁺ ion, 0·75	Na⁺ ion, 0·95	Cl⁻ ion, 1·81
Fe⁺⁺⁺ ion, 0·60		

The sizes given for the atoms are the covalent radii (see page 135).

2. Effect of Co-ordination Number on Ionic Radii.

The ionic radii given in Table 10 are based on the assumption that an ion may be regarded as a sphere.   This is not really accurate as, on the one hand, the arrangement of extra-nuclear electrons is rather diffuse, which makes it difficult to define the perimeter of an ion, and, on the other, two adjacent ions interact and cause deformation.

There are no grounds for assuming that the deformation of an ion is the same in one type of crystal arrangement as in another, and it is, therefore, necessary to allot slightly different ionic radii to ions when such ions occur in different crystal structures.   The values given in Table 10 are those for ions taking part in a crystal structure with a co-ordination number of 6.

Ammonium chloride crystallises with the sodium chloride structure (co-ordination number, 6) above 184·3° C. and with the caesium chloride structure (co-ordination number, 8) below that temperature, and there is found to be an interionic distance about 3% greater in the latter arrangement.   On these lines conversion factors can be worked out for converting the ionic radii for 6-fold co-ordination to ionic radii for any other co-ordination.   Thus for co-ordination number from 6 to 8 the factor is 1·03, and from 6 to 4 it is 0·94.　It will be seen that the changes are not very great.

3. Covalent Radii.

The interatomic distance between two atoms is not the same when the two atoms are joined (as ions) by an electrovalent bond as when they are linked by a covalent bond.　X-ray analysis of ionic crystals gives results for interionic distances which lead to the formulation of ionic radii as described in section 1.

Investigation of crystals with covalent lattices (see page 95) by X-rays, and of molecules by electron diffraction and spectroscopic methods, however, leads to measurement of the interatomic distance between two atoms linked by a covalent bond.

The main feature of such measurements is that the interatomic distance between two atoms A and B linked by a covalent bond is very nearly constant, and is independent of the varied nature of the molecules in which the bond length may be measured.　The C—Cl distance, for instance, is 1·76A in methyl chloride, methylene chloride, chloroform, and carbon tetrachloride.　Similarly, the C—C distance is 1·54A whether the bond occurs in diamond, propane, mesitylene, paraldehyde, or many other carbon compounds.

It is found, moreover, that the interatomic distance A—B is equal to the arithmetic mean of the distances A—A and B—B, i.e.

$$A—B = \frac{A—A + B—B}{2}$$

Cl—Cl, for instance, is 1·98A and, taking the C—C value as already given (1·54A) it follows that the C—Cl distance must be 1·76A, an exact agreement with the experimentally observed result.

Because this simple relationship is found to hold in many cases it is possible to allot what are called covalent radii to the elements such that $r_A + r_B = A—B$.　In the chlorine molecule, for instance, the interatomic distance is 1·98A and the covalent radius for chlorine is half this value, i.e. 0·99A. Similarly, the covalent radius for carbon is half 1·54, i.e. 0·77A, and the C—Cl distance given by r_C plus r_{Cl} is found, as before, to have the value 1·76A.

The covalent radii of those elements which normally form covalent bonds are summarised in Table 11.

TABLE 11

SINGLE-BOND COVALENT RADII

(Values in Angstrom units)

H 0·30	B 0·88	C 0·77	N 0·70	O 0·66	F 0·64
		Si 1·17	P 1·10	S 1·04	Cl 0·99
			As 1·21	Se 1·17	Br 1·14
			Sb 1·41	Te 1·37	I 1·33

It must be emphasised that the values given only refer to elements when they exhibit their normal covalencies, i.e. when they form only single bonds equal in number to the group number in which the element is placed in the periodic table. They are referred to as single-bond covalent radii or normal covalent radii.

As is to be expected, the heavier elements in any one group of the periodic table have the larger radii; the heavier elements contain more extra-nuclear electrons. For elements in the same horizontal periods those with higher atomic numbers have the smaller radii; these elements have their outer electrons in the same orbits, but the electrons are more strongly attracted by increasing positive charges on the nuclei.

The effects on covalent radii of the formation of multiple bonds, of the ionic character of a covalent bond, and of the different types of bond arrangement in crystals are discussed in the following sections.

4. Double and Triple Bonds. Measurement of the interatomic distance between two atoms joined by double or triple bonds leads to results similar to those obtained for single bonds. A double or triple bond between any two atoms has a constant length, and the arithmetic mean relationship holds as for single bonds.

It is therefore possible to assign double-bond or triple-bond covalent radii to the elements and some numerical values are given in Table 12.

TABLE 12

MULTIPLE-BOND COVALENT RADII

(Values in Angstrom units)

B= 0·76	C= 0·67	N= 0·60	O= 0·55
B≡ 0·68	C≡ 0·60	N≡ 0·55	O≡ 0·50
	Si= 1·07		S= 0·94

By comparing the values given with those in Table 11 for single-bond covalent radii it will be seen that the double-bond radius of an atom is about 13% and the triple-bond radius about 22% less than the corresponding single-bond radius.

5. Effect of Ionic Character on Normal Covalent Radii. The sum of the normal covalent radii of two atoms A and B only gives the bond length, A—B, when the bond is purely covalent or nearly so. In other cases the measured bond length is less than the sum of the covalent radii for the bonded atoms, an effect which is attributed to the partial ionic character of the bond (see page 86).

Schomaker and Stevenson have attempted to treat the effect quantitatively, and express the length of a bond A—B as

$$A—B = r_A + r_B - 0.09(x_A - x_B)$$

where r_A and r_B are the covalent radii of A and B, and x_A and x_B their respective electronegativities (see page 89). This expression, which is purely empirical, gives good agreement between calculated and measured bond lengths in many cases, but it fails to account for all the measured bond lengths.

6. Tetrahedral and Octahedral Radii. The single-bond covalent radii given in Table 11 refer to the elements only when they are exhibiting their normal covalency. So far as interatomic distances in crystals are concerned, however, the distance depends on the crystal type, and covalent radii for use in solid crystals are not necessarily the same as the normal covalent radii. This leads to the use of tetrahedral and octahedral covalent radii which apply to tetrahedrally and octahedrally arranged crystals respectively.

These values are sometimes exactly the same as the normal covalent radii, e.g. the tetrahedral radii for elements in the first and second periods of the periodic table are the same as the normal covalent radii for these elements, and in no case is there any great difference.

CHAPTER TEN

SIMPLE EXAMPLES OF RESONATING MOLECULES

1. Conditions for Resonance. The general idea of resonance has already been introduced (page 71) and in this chapter selected examples are taken to illustrate how experimental measurements demand that certain molecules must be represented as resonance hybrids.

In choosing the 'possible' structures for a molecule, certain conditions must be fulfilled so that resonance can occur. These conditions may be summarised as follows:

(a) The several 'possible' structures must have the various atoms in the same relative positions.* Resonance is concerned solely with the electrons.

(b) The several 'possible' structures must be reasonably stable. If very unstable, the contribution of the 'possible' structure to the actual structure will be so small as to be almost negligible. Thus H^-Cl^+ is a possible structure for hydrogen chloride but the Cl^+ ion is known to be so unstable that the structure is unimportant.

(c) The number of unpaired electrons must be the same in all 'possible' structures. Resonance demands the possibility of a continuous change from one bond type to another, but if two structures have different numbers of unpaired electrons the change between them will not be continuous as the electrons will have to pair and unpair.

* This condition serves to distinguish between resonance and tautomerism. The tautomeric forms of a substance have different arrangements of atoms; moreover, each kind of molecule can normally be isolated.

2. Carbon Dioxide. The formula of carbon dioxide was, for a long time, written as $O=C=O$ and, on general grounds, this seems to be perfectly satisfactory. The formula as written, however, does not fit in with the observed interatomic distances or the heats of formation.

The double-bond covalent radii of carbon and oxygen are 0·67A and 0·55A respectively (page 136) giving an inter-atomic distance for the $C=O$ bond of 1·22A. The observed distance between the oxygen and carbon atoms in carbon dioxide is, however, found to be 1·15A, and, therefore, the molecule cannot be satisfactorily represented by $O=C=O$. Other structures which might be possible are $O \leftarrow C \rightleftharpoons O$ and $O \rightleftharpoons C \rightarrow O$ which from the single-bond radii of carbon and oxygen (0·77A and 0·66A respectively) and the triple-bond radii (0·60A and 0·50A) have interatomic distances between carbon and oxygen atoms of 1·43A ($C \rightarrow O$) and 1·10A ($C \rightleftharpoons O$).

Representing carbon dioxide as a resonance hybrid between the three structures:

(a) $O=C=O$
(b) $O \leftarrow C \rightleftharpoons O$
(c) $O \rightleftharpoons C \rightarrow O$

will, therefore, explain the observed C—O distance of 1·15A, the three 'possible' structures contributing in such a way as to give this distance in the 'actual' molecule.

On the evidence from dipole moment measurements, the structures (b) and (c) must contribute equally so that the dipole moments they would each have individually will cancel out, for carbon dioxide is not found to have a dipole moment.

The existence of the suggested resonance hybrid is also confirmed from a consideration of heats of formation, for the calculated value for carbon dioxide on the assumption that the formula is simply $O=C=O$ is found to be 346 k.cal.

(bond energy C=O is 173, page 84), whereas the actual measured value is 383 k.cal.*

The increased stability of carbon dioxide over the structure O=C=O is explained as being due to the possibilities of resonance between the three structures, (a), (b), and (c). The value of 37 k.cal. is known as the *resonance energy* of the molecule. It may not be superfluous to mention again the important fact that the 'actual' structure of a resonance hybrid is more stable than any of the 'possible' structures (see page 72), and this example illustrates the general principle.

3. Benzene. The actual structure of the benzene molecule has been in some doubt for a very long time and numerous suggestions have been put forward to account for the known facts, but none of them have been entirely satisfactory. The generally accepted view has been that of Kekulé and the molecule has been regarded as 'oscillating' between the two structures represented by:

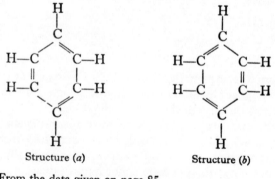

Structure (a)   Structure (b)

* From the data given on page 85,

$$C \text{ (solid)} + O_2 = CO_2 + 94 \cdot 45 \text{ k.cal.}$$
$$C \text{ (solid)} = C \text{ (atom)} - 170 \cdot 4 \text{ k.cal}$$
$$O_2 \text{ (gaseous)} = 2O \text{ (atoms)} - 118 \cdot 2 \text{ k.cal.}$$

It follows that

$$C \text{ (atom)} + 2O \text{ (atoms)} = CO_2 + 383 \cdot 05 \text{ k.cal.}$$

The modern view is that benzene is a resonance hybrid between these two 'possible' structures and this is supported by experimental measurements.

In the first place the observed distance between the carbon atoms is 1·39A, all the six bonds being the same. The normal distance between two carbon atoms joined by a single covalent bond is 1·54A (normal covalent radius of carbon $=0·77A$) and when joined by a double bond is 1·34A (double-bond covalent radius of carbon $=0·67A$). This clearly indicates that the actual bond between carbon atoms in the benzene molecule is something intermediate between a single and a double bond, i.e. benzene is a resonance hybrid between structures (a) and (b).

This conclusion is also supported by measurements of the heat of formation as compared with the calculated values. The actual measured heat of formation of benzene is 1,315 k.cal.,* but the value calculated by summing the bond energies of six C—H, three C—C, and three C=C bonds is only 1,276 k.cal. The actual benzene molecule is, therefore, more stable than either structure (a) or structure (b). It is,

---

* The heat of combustion of benzene is 789·2 k.cal., i.e

$$C_6H_6 + 7\tfrac{1}{2}O_2 = 6CO_2 + 3H_2O \text{ (liquid)} + 789·2 \text{ k.cal.}$$

From data given on page 85,

$$6C \text{ (solid)} + 6O_2 = 6CO_2 + 566·7 \text{ k.cal.}$$

and $$3H_2 \text{ (gaseous)} + 1\tfrac{1}{2}O_2 = 3H_2O \text{ (liquid)} + 205·14 \text{ k.cal.}$$

It follows that

$$6C \text{ (solid)} + 3H_2 \text{ (gaseous)} = C_6H_6 - 17·36 \text{ k.cal.}$$

But (page 85),

$$6C \text{ (solid)} = 6C \text{ (atoms)} - 1\,022·4 \text{ k.cal.}$$

and $$3H_2 \text{ (gaseous)} = 6H \text{ (atoms)} - 310·2 \text{ k.cal.}$$

Therefore,

$$6C \text{ (atoms)} + 6H \text{ (atoms)} = C_6H_6 + 1,315·24 \text{ k.cal.}$$

i.e. the measured heat of formation of benzene is 1,315 k.cal.

in fact, a resonance hybrid between the two structures with a resonance energy of 39 k.cal.

Other possible structures for benzene probably contribute to the resonance hybrid but they are so unstable as compared with structures (a) and (b) as to be relatively unimportant. Two such structures are shown:

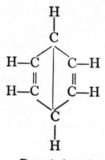

Dewar's formula

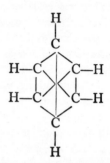

The centric formula of Armstrong, Baeyer, and Claus

The instability of these structures is due to the fact that they involve bonds between widely separated carbon atoms.

4. The Hydrides of Boron. The hydrides of boron have long been of interest from the point of view of valency as, assuming boron to be trivalent, they all seem to contain too much hydrogen as shown below:

Expected hydride

BH_3 B_2H_4 B_3H_5 B_4H_6 B_5H_7 B_6H_8 B_7H_9 B_8H_{10} B_9H_{11} $B_{10}H_{12}$

Known hydride

— B_2H_6 — B_4H_{10} B_5H_9 B_6H_{10} — — — $B_{10}H_{14}$
B_5H_{11}

Of the six known hydrides some contain two hydrogen atoms in excess of the expected number and the others four. It may be significant that those with four atoms in excess, i.e. B_4H_{10} and B_5H_{11}, are less stable than the others.

The simplest known hydride, B_2H_6, has the same type of

formula as ethane, C_2H_6, but there are not enough electrons in the boron compound to form seven covalent bonds as found in ethane.   Many suggestions have been put forward as to the arrangement of electrons in B_2H_6 and the other hydrides of boron but there is still some doubt as to the correct answer.

The measured B—B distance is 1·86A and the B—H distance, 1·27A.   A single covalent link between two boron atoms would be expected to have a length of 1·76A (normal covalent radius of boron=0·88A), and a double bond would be shorter still.   A single covalent bond between boron and hydrogen ought to have a length of 1·18A (single covalent radius of boron and hydrogen=0·88A and 0·30A respectively).

Sidgwick originally suggested that the molecule, B_2H_6, contained 1-electron links, e.g.

$$\begin{array}{cc} H & H \\ \circ\bullet & \times\circ \\ H \circ B \times B \circ H \\ \circ\bullet & \times\circ \\ H & H \end{array}$$

and this idea was extended to include all the various resonance possibilities, e.g.

$$\begin{array}{ccc} \begin{array}{cc} H & H \\ \circ\bullet & \times\circ \\ H \, {\circ\atop\bullet} B \times B \circ H \\ \circ\bullet & \times\circ \\ H & H \end{array} & \begin{array}{cc} H & H \\ \circ\bullet & \circ \\ H \, {\circ\atop\bullet} B \times B {\times\atop\circ} H \\ \circ & \times\circ \\ H & H \end{array} & \begin{array}{cc} H & H \\ \circ & \circ\times \\ H \, {\bullet\atop\circ} B \times B {\circ\atop\times} H \\ \circ\bullet & \circ \\ H & H \end{array} \end{array}$$

On this view the molecule is stabilised by resonance between the various 'possible' structures, and as none of the bonds in the actual molecule will be normal single covalent bonds there is no disagreement with the observed bond lengths.

Lewis (1933) considered the molecule as a resonance

hybrid between the various possibilities of which the following are examples:

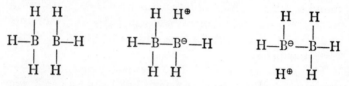

In 1939 it was suggested by Pauling that the 'Sidgwick' structures could resonate with the 'Lewis' structures, if the spins of the single electrons in the 1-electron bonds were paired with each other (see page 138).

More recent resonance possibilities include the structures,

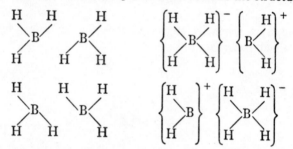

The latest developments, however, represent B_2H_6 as a so-called 'Bridge Structure',

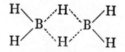

Spectroscopic evidence indicates that the two central hydrogen atoms lie above and below the two BH_2 groups, which are coplanar. These two central hydrogen atoms link the two BH_2 groups together, but the precise nature of the valency bonds joining the hydrogen atoms to the BH_2 groups is not fully understood: hence the dotted lines in the structure as shown.

It is thought that the higher hydrides of boron also involve 'Bridge Structures'.

5. Further Examples. Some other examples of molecules best represented as resonance hybrids are given below, the evidence being presented briefly in each case.

(*a*) *Carbon monoxide.* Resonance hybrid between

$$C{=}O \qquad\qquad C{\equiv}O$$

Structure 1 Structure 2

The calculated bond distances for structures 1 and 2 are 1·22A and 1·10A respectively (see page 136), whereas the measured bond distance is 1·13A.

The heat of formation of the C=O bond is 173 k.cal. (see page 84), whereas the observed heat of formation for carbon monoxide is 256 k.cal., the resonance energy being 83 k.cal.

Carbon monoxide has a dipole moment which is very nearly zero whereas both structure 1 and structure 2 would have large dipole moments if they existed individually.

(*b*) *The carbonate ion.* Resonance hybrid between

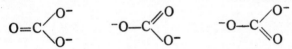

The calculated bond length for the C=O bond is 1·22A and for the C—O bond 1·43A. The observed bond length in the carbonate ion is 1·31A. The resonance energy is 42 k.cal.

(*c*) *The nitrate ion.* Resonance hybrid between

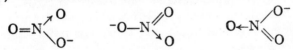

These structures are very similar to those given for the carbonate ion. The observed bond length is 1·21A; the calculated bond length for N—O is 1·36A and for N=O 1·15A. The resonance energy is 45 k.cal.

(*d*) *Nitrous oxide*.   Resonance hybrid between

$$N\leftarrow N=O \qquad\qquad N\equiv N\rightarrow O$$

Structure 1   Structure 2

The calculated bond lengths for the various bonds involved in these two structures are,

$N\leftarrow N$	1·20A	$N=O$	1·15A
$N\equiv N$	1·10A	$N\rightarrow O$	1·36A

The length of the molecule, which is linear, as actually measured is 2·31A, the probable bond lengths being N—N, 1·12A, and N—O, 1·19A.

The dipole moment of nitrous oxide is very small so that the two structures must contribute almost equally.

(*e*) *Nitric oxide*.   The structure of nitric oxide has already been given (page 42) as involving a 3-electron bond. This is really a convenient way of representing resonance between the two structures,

$\overset{\times}{\underset{\times}{\times}}N\overset{\times}{\underset{\times}{}}\colon\overset{\bullet\bullet}{O}\colon \qquad\qquad\qquad \overset{\times\bullet}{\underset{\times}{\times}}N\overset{\times}{\underset{\times}{\bullet}}\colon\overset{\bullet}{O}\colon$

The observed bond distance in nitric oxide is 1·14A. The bond length for the $N=O$ bond would be expected to be 1·15A and for the $N\equiv O$ bond 1·05A.

(*f*) *The sulphate ion*.   In the sulphate ion the four oxygen atoms are arranged around the central sulphur atom almost tetrahedrally The measured bond distance is 1·51A. The calculated bond distance is 1·70A, assuming single bonds between the sulphur and oxygen atoms, and 1·49A assuming double bonds.

It is clear that there must be some double bond character about the bonds in the ion, and it is best represented as a resonance hybrid between many various structures. Typical 'possible' structures are:

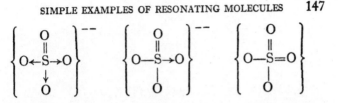

The last of these structures is probably the most important but there are many other similar 'possible' structures for the double bonds have many alternative positions. It must be emphasised that all the four bonds in the 'actual' structure are alike.

Other ions and molecules in which the actual bonds are probably intermediate between single and double bonds are SiO_4^{--}, PO_4^{---}, ClO_4^-, $POCl_3$, and SO_2Cl_2.

CHAPTER ELEVEN

HYDROGEN AND THE HYDROGEN BOND

1. The Valency of Hydrogen. Hydrogen can enter into chemical combination with other elements or radicals in five distinct ways as follows:

    (*a*) by forming a cation, H^+,
    (*b*) by forming an anion, H^-,
    (*c*) by forming a normal covalent bond, H—,
    (*d*) by forming a 1-electron bond, H·, and
    (*e*) by forming a hydrogen bond, H·····.

Each of these types of bond formation will be discussed in turn.

(*a*) *Formation of H^+ cations.* The H^+ ion is formed from a hydrogen atom by the loss of an electron and it is simply a proton (see page 111). In the presence of water it is invariably hydrated to form an $[H_3O]^+$ ion with a structure represented by

$$\left[H \leftarrow O \begin{matrix} \diagup H \\ \diagdown H \end{matrix} \right]^+$$

This ion is called the hydroxonium or hydronium ion and is normally what is meant when reference is made to a hydrogen ion. By hydration, the bare proton attains the electronic structure of helium.

The hydroxonium ion is present in solutions of all acids in water, and an acid can be defined as a substance which when dissolved in water produces this ion, e.g.

$$HCl + H_2O \rightarrow [H_3O]^+ + Cl^-$$
$$H_2SO_4 + 2H_2O \rightarrow 2[H_3O]^+ + SO_4^{--}$$

The measurement of the concentration of hydrogen ions in solution affords a method of determining the strength of acids.

(b) *Formation of H⁻ anions.* The negatively charged ion of hydrogen is formed from a hydrogen atom by the gain of one electron and it has the electronic structure of helium. It is present in a series of metallic hydrides known as the salt-like hydrides. Such hydrides are formed, as colourless crystals, by the alkali and alkaline earth metals simply by heating the metal in hydrogen:

$$LiH \quad NaH \quad KH \quad RbH \quad CsH$$
$$CaH_2 \quad SrH_2 \quad BaH_2$$

The alkali metal hydrides have the same crystal structure as sodium chloride, the chloride ions, Cl^-, being replaced by the hydride ions, H^-. Further evidence of the existence of the H^- ion is provided by the fact that electrolysis of molten lithium hydride using steel electrodes produces lithium at the cathode and hydrogen at the anode. Lithium hydride must, therefore, be represented as an electro-valent compound, Li^+H^-, and similarly for the other hydrides.

(c) *Formation of normal covalent bond, H—.* The hydrogen atom has a single electron which can be shared with another electron to form a single covalent bond, the hydrogen thereby attaining an inert gas (helium) structure. Hydrogen chloride, for example, has the structure

$$H \overset{\times\ \times}{\underset{\times\ \times}{\overset{\bullet}{\times}}} Cl \overset{\times}{\times}$$

and the hydrogen molecule also contains this type of bond, $H \overset{\bullet}{\underset{\times}{}} H$.

This type of valency bond is to be found in the great

majority of the hydrides of the elements known as the molecular or volatile hydrides, and including

B_2H_6	CH_4	NH_3	H_2O	HF
	SiH_4	PH_3	H_2S	HCl
	GeH_4	AsH_3	H_2Se	HBr
	SnH_4	SbH_3	H_2Te	HI
	PbH_4	BiH_3	(H_2Po)	

(*d*) *Formation of a* 1-*electron bond*, *H*·. The existence of a valency bond made up of a single electron is very unusual. It undoubtedly occurs, however, in the hydrogen molecule-ion, H_2^+ (see page 41) and, possibly, in the hydrides of boron, which are discussed on page 143.

(*e*) *Formation of a hydrogen bond*, *H*·····. This type of bond formation is dealt with in the following section.

2. The Hydrogen Bond. Normally a hydrogen atom can form only one valency bond, but there are certain compounds in which it appears to form two bonds.

Hydrogen fluoride, for instance, is known, from molecular weight determinations, to be associated, i.e. to exist as $(HF)_n$ and not simply as HF, and the acid salt potassium hydrogen fluoride, KHF_2, is well known. Originally $(HF)_n$ and KHF_2 were formulated by assuming that hydrogen could act as an acceptor and form a dative bond with fluorine acting as the donor:

$$(H—F \rightarrow H—F \rightarrow H—F)_n \qquad K^+(F \rightarrow H—F)^-$$

There is, however, no reason to assume that a hydrogen atom can act as an acceptor in this way for it has only one stable orbit (1*s*) which can only hold two electrons, and the formulæ as written above give the hydrogen atoms four electrons.

The linkage previously represented as a dative bond is now regarded as a special type of bond known as a hydrogen bond. The mechanism of its formation is thought to be electrostatic. The bifluoride ion, for instance, is envisaged as shown in Fig. 33, the two negatively charged fluoride ions being linked by the positively charged hydrogen ion (proton).

To distinguish a hydrogen bond it is probably best to write it as a dotted line so that the bifluoride ion becomes $[F\cdots H-F]^-$, and, in general, when a hydrogen bond links two atoms X and Y the structure is represented as $X-H\cdots Y$, or, more accurately, as a resonance hybrid between $X-H\cdots Y$ and $X\cdots H-Y$.

That this electrostatic mechanism for the formation of hydrogen bonds is probably correct is shown by the fact that the bond is only formed by the most electronegative elements, chiefly by nitrogen, oxygen, and fluorine. Moreover, the element with the highest electro-negativity, i.e. fluorine, has the greatest tendency to form hydrogen bonds. The hydrogen bonds involving fluorine are the strongest hydrogen bonds known but their strength (approximately 5–10 k.cal.)

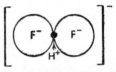

FIG. 33. The bifluoride ions, $[HF_2]^-$

is very small as compared with that of normal covalent bonds (approximately 50–100 k.cal.).

Other examples of compounds in which a hydrogen bond is thought to be formed are listed below, with some of the evidence which points to the existence of the bond.

(a) *Ice*. The crystal structure of ice shows a tetrahedral arrangement of water molecules similar to that found in the wurtzite structure (page 96). Each oxygen atom is surrounded tetrahedrally by four others and it is supposed that hydrogen bonds link pairs of oxygen atoms together as shown in Fig. 34.

The distance between adjacent oxygen atoms is 2·76A and this points to the fact that the hydrogen atom linking the two oxygen atoms together is not midway between them for the O—H distance in water vapour is 0·96A, and not half 2·76. Distance measurements on other compounds, too, indicate that the hydrogen atom in a hydrogen bond is not equidistant from the two atoms being linked.

The arrangement of the water molecules in ice is a very open structure and this explains the low density of ice. When ice melts, the structure begins to break down and some of the molecules pack more closely together so that water has a higher density than ice, with a maximum at 4° C. Some

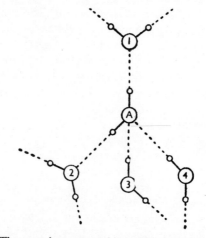

Fig. 34. The crystal structure of ice. The central oxygen atom, A, is surrounded tetrahedrally by the oxygen atoms, 1, 2, 3 and 4. All other oxygen atoms are arranged similarly. The hydrogen atoms are shown as small circles, and the dotted lines indicate the hydrogen bonds

molecules in water are, however, still linked together by hydrogen bonds.

(b) *Hydrides of fluorine, oxygen, and nitrogen.* The association of hydrogen fluoride has already been mentioned and similar association is found in water and ammonia. This shows itself in the high dielectric constants of these three hydrides (see page 66), and also in their abnormal melting and boiling points when compared with other hydrides in the same groups of the periodic table. The values are given in Fig. 35.

The high melting points and boiling points of HF, H_2O, and NH_3 are due to association caused by the formation of hydrogen bonds. Methane has a normal value; it is not associated as carbon is not sufficiently electronegative to form hydrogen bonds.

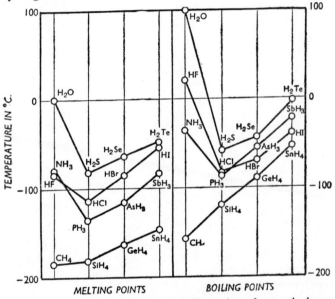

FIG. 35. The abnormal melting and boiling points of water, hydrogen fluoride and ammonia

(c) *Carboxylic acids.* Many carboxylic acids are known to associate in certain solvents and to give correspondingly high molecular weight results. This association is attributed to hydrogen bond formation, as, for instance, in formic acid

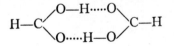

where electron diffraction measurements show this arrangement of atoms and give the O—O distance as 2·67A.

In certain solvents this type of association takes place, not between two molecules of the solute, but between one of the solute and one of the solvent. Benzoic acid, for example, is associated in benzene and carbon tetrachloride but links up with the solvent in acetic acid and acetone.

(*d*) *Intramolecular hydrogen bonds.* It might be expected that association similar to that known to occur in carboxylic acids would occur, for instance, in salicylaldehyde or o-nitro phenol, but this is not found since hydrogen bonds can conveniently form within the molecule as shown below:

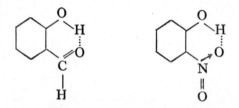

Direct evidence for the formation of such bonds is provided by a study of the infra-red absorption spectra of the molecules. A normal hydroxyl group is found to give rise to a particular band in the spectrum, but this band is not observed when the hydroxyl group is involved in hydrogen bond formation. Salicylaldehyde and o-nitro phenol do not give the normal hydroxyl group spectrum, but m- and p-hydroxybenzaldehyde and m- and p-nitro phenol do, for it is only in the ortho substituted compounds that hydrogen bonds can be formed within the molecule.

The formation of such bonds affects the properties of ortho substituted compounds as compared with the other isomers, and it is for this reason that the phenomenon is sometimes called the ortho effect. Ortho-nitro phenol, for instance, is less soluble in water than the meta and para forms as the hydroxylic character of the substance is suppressed by the formation of hydrogen bonds.   There are many other facts which can be explained in the same way.

Sufficient has been said to indicate that formation of hydrogen bonds is fairly widespread amongst electronegative elements, and that there is a variety of experimental evidence which points to the formation of such bonds.

The hydrogen bond may be a weak one, but as more and more is learnt about it, it assumes an increasingly important place in modern valency theory.   It is, too, very closely related to life, for many biological processes are now thought to involve hydrogen bonding.

CHAPTER TWELVE

MOLECULAR ORBITALS

1. Introduction. Valency bonds have been considered so far in terms of what is known as the valency-bond theory or the method of atomic orbitals (orbits). The complicated arrangement of electrons in a molecule is thought of in direct relation to the simpler arrangements in the separate component atoms. It has been emphasised that, when the electronic arrangement in a molecule cannot be conveniently represented, it is thought of as a resonance hybrid between various simpler structures, which can be represented by well-established methods.

This treatment was the first to be popularised and, as we have seen, it has led to many important developments. A second line of approach is afforded, however, by the method of molecular orbitals. In this method, a molecule is supposed to have various electronic orbitals associated with it, in much the same way as a single atom has. All, or nearly all, of the electrons originally associated with the separate atoms in a molecule are supposed to enter the various molecular orbitals, which fill up according to certain rules just as atomic orbitals do (page 26). Each electron is regarded as part of the new framework of molecular orbitals, though not all the electrons contribute to the binding together of the atoms in the molecule.

In effect, the method of molecular orbitals envisages a more complete interaction between the electrons in atomic orbitals than the valency bond theory does. The conception of a 'united atom' is used, and this supposes a complete coalescence of the nuclei of the separate atoms concerned. An over-simplified pictorial representation is given in Fig. 36, which shows the arrangement in two separate atoms, A and B, the arrangement in the corresponding 'united atom,' $A+B$, and the arrangement in the molecule, AB. The molecular orbital method considers this molecule as being

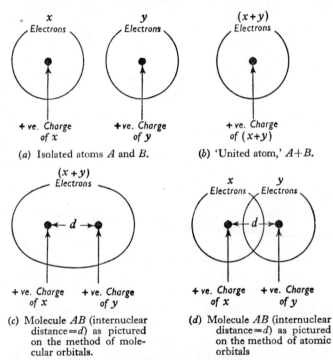

(a) Isolated atoms A and B.

(b) 'United atom,' $A+B$.

(c) Molecule AB (internuclear distance=d) as pictured on the method of molecular orbitals.

(d) Molecule AB (internuclear distance=d) as pictured on the method of atomic orbitals

Fig. 36.   Representation of formation of " united atom ", A + B, and molecule, AB, from isolated atoms, A and B

derived from the 'united atom,' whereas the valency-bond theory considers it as arising from the normal A and B atoms.

The matter is considered further in the following sections. Fortunately, the great majority of the results obtained by applying the two distinct methods to valency problems are the same.   Both methods involve approximations, and any particular problem may be more amenable to treatment by the one method than by the other.

2. Energy Levels of Molecular Orbitals. In the method of molecular orbitals, the s, p, d orbitals in a single atom are replaced by σ, π, and δ orbitals in a molecule. The application of the Pauli principle (page 26) means that any particular molecular orbital can only contain two electrons, and that these two must have different spins. Consideration of the energy levels of the various molecular orbitals controls the way in which electrons are allotted to them in any molecule.

The energy levels of the orbitals in a molecule, A_2, are considered in relation to the energy levels of (a) the atomic orbitals of the separated A atoms, and (b) the atomic orbitals of the 'united atom,' $A + A$.

Such a 'united atom' will have a nuclear charge twice as high as that of a single A atom, and this means that the energy levels of the s, p, d orbitals allotted to the 'united atom' will not be the same as the levels of the corresponding orbitals in the single atoms. The fact that the 'united atom' contains twice as many electrons as a single atom also means that some electrons must be 'promoted' when the 'united atom' is formed from two single atoms. Two single atoms, for example, each with two $1s$ electrons, would give a 'united atom' with four electrons. Only two of these four can be allotted to the $1s$ level of the 'united atom' as this level can only hold two; the remaining two electrons must be 'promoted' to $2s$ or higher levels.

The relation of the energy levels of molecular orbitals to those of the atomic orbitals of the single and united atoms is summarised diagrammatically in what is known as a correlation diagram (Fig. 37).

It will be seen that the energy levels of the molecular orbitals are somewhere intermediate between those of the atomic orbitals of the single and united atoms, and that the energy varies as the internuclear distance between the two atoms concerned changes from infinity, for the two separated atoms, to zero, for the united atom.

Some of the molecular orbitals are related to falling correlation lines (1s to 1s, for instance), and some to rising

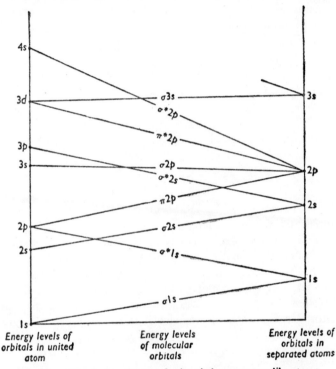

FIG. 37. Correlation diagram for bonds between two like atoms

lines (1s to 2p, for instance). Those molecular orbitals corresponding to falling lines are bonding orbitals causing attraction between the atoms concerned; those corresponding to rising lines are anti-bonding and cause repulsion between the atoms. In other words, electrons which have to be

12

promoted in passing from the single atoms to the united atom normally occupy anti-bonding orbitals.

The most commonly occupied molecular orbitals are named as follows:

Bonding orbitals　．　．　$\sigma 1s$　　$\sigma 2s$　　$\pi 2p$　　$\sigma 2p$
Anti-bonding orbitals　．　$\sigma^* 1s$　　$\sigma^* 2s$　　$\pi^* 2p$　　$\sigma^* 2p$

and this nomenclature indicates the atomic orbitals normally related to a particular molecular orbital.†

The π orbitals are further subdivided just as p atomic orbitals are (page 27). Thus a $\pi 2p$ orbital is subdivided into $\pi_y 2p$ and $\pi_z 2p$ depending on whether the orbital is formed from p_y or p_x atomic orbitals.

For simple diatomic molecules, formed between two like atoms, the order in which the various molecular orbitals fill up, i.e. the order of their energy levels, is

$$\sigma 1s \quad \sigma^* 1s \quad \sigma 2s \quad \sigma^* 2s \quad \sigma 2p \quad \begin{matrix} \pi_y 2p \\ \pi_z 2p \end{matrix} \quad \begin{matrix} \pi_y^* 2p \\ \pi_z^* 2p \end{matrix} \quad \sigma^* 2p$$

This sequence enables the electronic structures of simple molecules to be considered.

3. Bonds Between Two Like Atoms. In the formation of the hydrogen molecule, H_2, the two $1s$ electrons, one from each of the two atoms concerned, pass into a $\sigma 1s$ molecular orbital. This is a bonding orbital and constitutes the single covalent bond in the hydrogen molecule. Since the $\sigma 1s$ orbital can only hold two electrons if they have different

† An alternative system of nomenclature, due to Mulliken, designates molecular orbitals as z, y, x, w, v, u orbitals in the order of their increasing energy. The sequence

$$\sigma 2s \qquad \sigma^* 2s \qquad \sigma 2p \qquad \begin{matrix} \pi_y 2p \\ \pi_z 2p \end{matrix} \qquad \begin{matrix} \pi_y^* 2p \\ \pi_z^* 2p \end{matrix} \qquad \sigma^* 2p$$

becomes

$$z\sigma \qquad y\sigma \qquad x\sigma \qquad w\pi \qquad v\pi \qquad u\sigma.$$

$\sigma 1s$ and $\sigma^* 1s$ orbitals are called $K(z\sigma)$ and $K(y\sigma)$; $\sigma 3s$ and $\sigma^* 3s$ orbitals, $M(z\sigma)$ and $M(y\sigma)$. The K and M denote the principal quantum number (page 24) of the atomic orbitals normally concerned.

spins (page 158), it is clear that a molecule will only be formed from two hydrogen atoms containing electrons with opposed spins. Atoms having electrons with like spins will not combine.

A helium molecule, He_2, cannot exist, because two of the four available $1s$ electrons pass into a $\sigma 1s$ bonding orbital, while the other two pass into a $\sigma^* 1s$ anti-bonding orbital. The filled bonding orbital counteracts the filled anti-bonding orbital, so that no bond results.

The filling up of the various molecular orbitals in other simple diatomic molecules containing like atoms is summarised in Fig. 38.

Orbital	H_2	(He_2)	N_2	O_2	F_2	(Ne_2)
$\sigma 1s$	2	2				
$\sigma^* 1s$		2		Not occupied		
$\sigma 2s$			2	2	2	2
$\sigma^* 2s$			2	2	2	2
$\sigma 2p$			2	2	2	2
$\pi_y 2p$			2	2	2	2
$\pi_z 2p$			2	2	2	2
$\pi_y^* 2p$				1	2	2
$\pi_z^* 2p$				1	2	2
$\sigma^* 2p$						2
Excess of bonding over anti-bonding electrons .	2	0	6	4	2	0
Normal covalency of atoms concerned . .	1	0	3	2	1	0

FIG. 38.   The filling up of molecular orbitals in simple diatomic molecules

It will be seen that molecular orbitals fill up according to their energy levels, just as atomic orbitals do in the formation of various atoms (page 27). The table, just given, does for molecules what Table 1 (page 29) does for atoms.

Notice that a single covalent bond is identified with the existence of a number of fully occupied bonding orbitals one greater than the number of fully occupied anti-bonding orbitals. A double bond corresponds with two fully occupied bonding orbitals more than the number of fully occupied anti-bonding orbitals; and so on.

A more detailed representation of any one molecule can be given in the way as shown for nitrogen in Fig. 39.

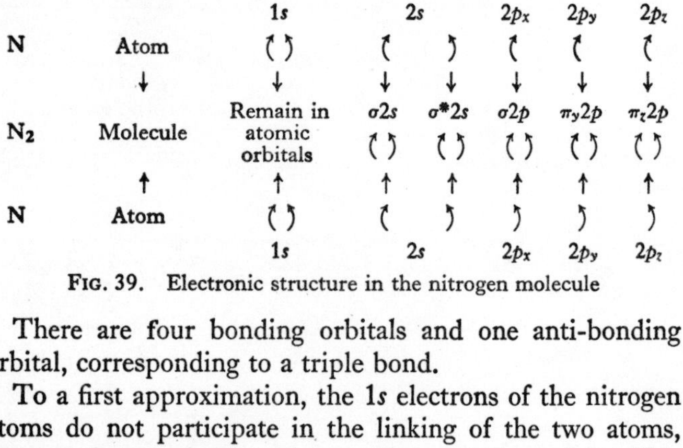

		$1s$		$2s$	$2p_x$	$2p_y$	$2p_z$
N	Atom	( )	(	)	(	(	(
↓		↓	↓	↓	↓	↓	↓
N_2	Molecule	Remain in atomic orbitals	$\sigma 2s$	$\sigma^* 2s$	$\sigma 2p$	$\pi_y 2p$	$\pi_z 2p$
			( )	( )	( )	( )	( )
↑		↑	↑	↑	↑	↑	↑
N	Atom	( )	(	)	)	)	)
		$1s$		$2s$	$2p_x$	$2p_y$	$2p_z$

FIG. 39. Electronic structure in the nitrogen molecule

There are four bonding orbitals and one anti-bonding orbital, corresponding to a triple bond.

To a first approximation, the $1s$ electrons of the nitrogen atoms do not participate in the linking of the two atoms, because they are held so close to their atomic nuclei. This is so for all electrons in an innermost atomic shell, and such electrons need not be represented as in molecular orbitals. The molecular structure of nitrogen may be written in an abbreviated form as $N_2\{KK(\sigma 2s)^2(\sigma^* 2s)^2(\sigma 2p)^2(\pi_y 2p)^2(\pi^z 2p)^2\}$, the KK indicating that the electrons in the $K(1)$ shell of the nitrogen atoms are not playing any part in bond formation, and $(\sigma 2s)^2$, for example, indicating the presence of two electrons in the $\sigma 2s$ molecular orbital.

4. Bonds Between Two Unlike Atoms. A consideration of bonding between two unlike atoms is not so simple as that between two like atoms. The energy levels of the atomic orbitals of the two separated unlike atoms are not equal, and this means that the energy levels of the molecular orbitals do not necessarily follow the sequence given on page 160.

Moreover, it is often difficult to calculate the actual energy levels of the various molecular orbitals concerned. This is mainly because the electrons allotted to the molecular orbitals do not originate from s or p or d atomic orbitals but from combinations between them. This introduces the idea of hybrid bonds in much the same way as in the method of atomic orbitals.

If the two atoms concerned are not very dissimilar, however, the molecular structure may not be very complicated. In particular, two molecules which have the same total number of electrons have similar molecular orbitals; this is the so-called isoelectronic principle.

The structure of carbon monoxide (with 14 electrons, 6 from the carbon and 8 from the oxygen), for example, is similar to that of nitrogen (with 14 electrons, 7 from each nitrogen atom). There is a slight difference, however, as carbon monoxide has a small dipole moment (pp. 127 and 145) and this has to be accounted for by the introduction of hybrid bonds.

5. Paramagnetism of Oxygen. Oxygen is one of the few gases which are strongly paramagnetic, and this distinctive property has recently been used in designing a magnetic analyser to determine the proportion of oxygen in a gaseous mixture.

A satisfactory molecular structure for oxygen must account forth is paramagnetism, and this means (p. 67) that there must be unpaired electrons in the molecule.

The method of atomic orbitals would, in its most direct

application, lead to a complete pairing of all electrons, the O_2 molecule being represented, by the method given on page 78, as containing a double bond:

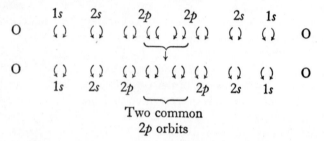

Two common
2p orbits

A molecule with such a structure would not, however, be paramagnetic as there are no unpaired electrons. The actual structure of oxygen has, therefore, been represented as containing two 3-electron bonds (page 42) and one single covalent bond:

The oxygen molecule contains two unpaired electrons when represented in this way.

The method of molecular orbitals provides a good answer to the problem quite straightforwardly and this was one of the earliest successes of the method.

The O_2 structure is given as

$$O_2\{KK(\sigma 2s)^2(\sigma^*2s)^2(\sigma 2p)^2(\pi_y 2p)^2(\pi_z 2p)^2(\pi_y^*2p)(\pi_z^*2p)\}$$

and the way in which this is built up from two oxygen atoms is shown in Fig. 40.

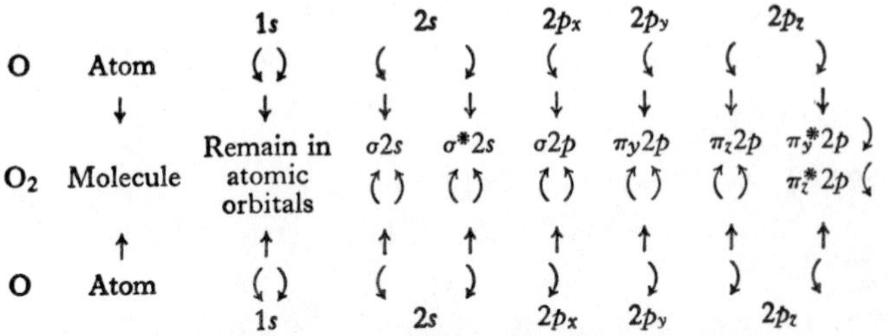

FIG. 40. Electronic structure in the oxygen molecule

The lower molecular orbitals fill up quite normally but there are only two electrons available for the π_y^*2p and π_z^*2p orbitals which, together, could hold four. If the two electrons were both allotted to either the π_y^*2p or the π_z^*2p orbital all electrons would be paired. The application of the rule of maximum multiplicity (page 28) shows, however, that one electron must be allotted to each orbital, and this means that the molecule contains two unpaired electrons.

The paramagnetism of sulphur and of nitric oxide is accounted for in a similar way.

RADII AND ENERGY LEVELS OF STATIONARY STATES IN THE HYDROGEN ATOM

1. Bohr's Treatment. In order to calculate the radii and energies of the stationary states, Bohr made the arbitrary assumption that the angular momentum of an electron in any stationary state must be an integral multiple of $\dfrac{h}{2\pi}$.

There is no a priori justification for this, but by using the assumption Bohr was able to obtain theoretical results in close agreement with experimental observations. The various simple calculations are carried out as follows.

(*a*) *Radii of Stationary States.* Angular momentum of electron of mass, *m*, travelling with velocity, *v*, in a circular orbit of radius, *r*,

$$= m.v.r \quad .$$

Therefore on Bohr's assumption

$$m.v.r = \frac{n \cdot h}{2\pi} \quad . \quad . \quad . \quad . \quad . \quad \text{(i)}$$

Attractive force between nucleus (charge, $+e$) and electron (charge, $-e$)

$$= \frac{e^2}{r^2} \quad . \quad . \quad . \quad . \quad . \quad \text{(ii)}$$

Therefore potential energy of electron

$$= \int_{\infty}^{r} \frac{e^2}{r^2} = -\frac{e^2}{r}.$$

(The negative sign indicates that work must be done to remove the electron away from the nucleus.)

Acceleration of electron towards centre of orbit

$$= \frac{v^2}{r}.$$

Therefore, force on the electron

$$= \frac{m \cdot v^2}{r}.$$

As the electron remains in its circular orbit, this force must be equal to the attractive force between the nucleus and the electron, therefore,

$$\frac{m \cdot v^2}{r} = \frac{e^2}{r^2}.$$

Kinetic energy of the electron

$$= \tfrac{1}{2} m \cdot v^2 = \frac{e^2}{2r} \quad \cdots \quad \text{(iii)}$$

Total energy of electron = potential energy + kinetic energy

$$= - \frac{e^2}{r} + \frac{e^2}{2r} = - \frac{e^2}{2r}. \quad \cdots \quad \text{(iv)}$$

From (i) and (iii) it follows that $r = \frac{n^2 \cdot h^2}{4\pi^2 \cdot e^2 \cdot m}$ and this expression gives the values of the radii of each stationary state, n having values 1, 2, 3 . . . etc.

For $n = 1$ and using the values $h = 6 \cdot 624 \times 10^{-27}$ erg-sec., $e = 4 \cdot 8025 \times 10^{-10}$ e.s.u., and $m = 9 \cdot 1066 \times 10^{-28}$ grams, the value of the radius obtained is $0 \cdot 529 \times 10^{-8}$ cm.

(b) *Energy of stationary states.* Substituting the expression for r into the expression for the total energy of the electron given in (iv) it follows that,

$$\text{Total energy of electron} = - \frac{2\pi^2 \cdot e^4 \cdot m}{n^2 \cdot h^2}.$$

Using the numerical values given above this leads to an energy of $217 \cdot 9 \times 10^{-13}$ ergs when $n=1$, and $54 \cdot 48 \times 10^{-13}$ ergs when $n=2$ (see Fig. 2, page 22).

In general the change in energy when an electron passes from an orbit, $n=n_2$, to an orbit, $n=n_1$, is given by

$$\frac{2\pi^2 \cdot e^4 \cdot m}{h^2}\left(\frac{1}{n_1^2} - \frac{1}{n_2^2}\right) \quad \cdots \quad (v)$$

This corresponds to radiation of wave-length λ given by

$$\frac{1}{\lambda} = \frac{2\pi^2 \cdot e^4 \cdot m}{c \cdot h^3}\left(\frac{1}{n_1^2} - \frac{1}{n_2^2}\right).$$

This expression for the wave-length of the radiation causing a line in the hydrogen spectrum corresponds to the empirical expression relating the lines in the various spectral series, $\frac{1}{\lambda} = R\left(\frac{1}{n_1^2} - \frac{1}{n_2^2}\right)$, given on page 19. It follows that R, known as the Rydberg constant, should be found equal to $\frac{2\pi^2 \cdot e^4 \cdot m}{c \cdot h^3}$ if the Bohr treatment is accurate. This is, in fact, so; the experimental value of R is 109,678, whilst the calculated value is 109,600.

(c) *Ionisation energy.* The expression given at (v) also enables the ionisation energy of hydrogen to be calculated. This represents (see page 54) the energy required to remove the electron in its normal state away from the atom, i.e. to infinity. Thus in the expression, (v), $n_2 = \infty$ and $n_1 = 1$ so that the ionisation energy is given by $\frac{2\pi^2 \cdot e^4 \cdot m}{h^2}$, which gives the value of $217 \cdot 9 \times 10^{-13}$ ergs, i.e. $13 \cdot 71$ electron-volts or 316 k.cal., as is observed.

2. Wave Mechanical Treatment (see page 29). In the wave mechanical treatment, the idea of a definite fixed stationary state of radius $0 \cdot 529 \times 10^{-8}$ cm. in the normal hydrogen atom is replaced by a less definite idea, and the electron is envisaged as existing in a more diffuse region round the nucleus. The probability of finding the electron at any one point in this diffuse region can be calculated from the wave function for the system. If the probability is plotted against the distance from the nucleus, as in Fig. 41, it is found that there is the greatest probability of finding the electron at a distance of 0.529×10^{-8} cm. from the nucleus.

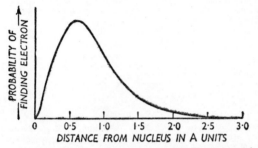

Fig. 41. The probability of finding the electron in a normal hydrogen atom at various distances from the nucleus

The electron is not, however, always to be found at this distance as supposed by Bohr.

In the same way the Bohr treatment gave the electron a constant speed within its circular orbit of 2.182×10^8 cm./sec., but the wave mechanical results indicate a variable speed ranging around this value.

The values for the energy of the electron in its various orbits are, similarly, found to be the same both on the Bohr and the wave mechanical treatment.

INDEX

		1s	2s	2p	3s	3p	3d	4s	4p	4d	4f	5s	5p	5d	6s	6p	6d	7s
	1 H	1																
	2 He	2																
	3 Li	2	1															
	4 Be	2	2															
	5 B	2	2	1														
	6 C	2	2	2														
	7 N	2	2	3														
	8 O	2	2	4														
	9 F	2	2	5														
	10 Ne	2	2	6														
	11 Na	2	8		1													
	12 Mg	2	8		2													
	13 Al	2	8		2	1												
	14 Si	2	8		2	2												
	15 P	2	8		2	3												
	16 S	2	8		2	4												
	17 Cl	2	8		2	5												
	18 A	2	8		2	6												
Transition elements	19 K	2	8		8			1										
	20 Ca	2	8		8			2										
	21 Sc	2	8		8		1	2										
	22 Ti	2	8		8		2	2										
	23 V	2	8		8		3	2										
	24 Cr	2	8		8		5	1										
	25 Mn	2	8		8		5	2										
	26 Fe	2	8		8		6	2										
	27 Co	2	8		8		7	2										
	28 Ni	2	8		8		8	2										
	29 Cu	2	8		8		10	1										
	30 Zn	2	8		8		10	2										
	31 Ga	2	8		18			2	1									
	32 Ge	2	8		18			2	2									
	33 As	2	8		18			2	3									
	34 Se	2	8		18			2	4									
	35 Br	2	8		18			2	5									
	36 Kr	2	8		18			2	6									
Transition elements	37 Rb	2	8		18			8				1						
	38 Sr	2	8		18			8				2						
	39 Y	2	8		18			8		1		2						
	40 Zr	2	8		18			8		2		2						
	41 Nb	2	8		18			8		4		1						
	42 Mo	2	8		18			8		5		1						
	43 Tc	2	8		18			8		6		1						
	44 Ru	2	8		18			8		7		1						
	45 Rh	2	8		18			8		8		1						
	46 Pd	2	8		18			8		10								